THE VIA ADVENT

Shawn Small

Providence House Publishers
WWW.PROVIDENCEHOUSE.COM
FRANKLIN, TENNESSEE

14   13   12   11   10   1   2   3   4   5

Library of Congress Control Number: 2010938952

ISBN: 978-1-57736-442-9

Cover illustration by Jenny Slaver

Cover and page design by LeAnna Massingille

PROVIDENCE HOUSE PUBLISHERS
238 Seaboard Lane • Franklin, Tennessee 37067
www.providencehouse.com
800-321-5692

For

Cheryl Small
who has been, for the last
two decades, my greatest source
of encouragement and strength.

Walter Boyd
who has walked the way of Christ,
by my side, from my first epiphany.

Christopher Small
who will always be the most precious
Christmas gift given to our family.

Contents

Foreword

foreword

The *Via Advent* is the hush you feel when you hear a single baby cry on Christmas eve and wait for the echoes to fade; it is the mystery that names you as the heir of Mary and Joseph. From the first lines of this magnificent work we are caught up in one divine idea: incarnation.

As I made my way through the book, I had to divorce myself from the mundane habit of mere reading, which I was doing when I began. It is a rare writer that makes me forget my petty rituals of life. But Shawn has done just that, even though I don't think he intended to. He simply loves the Christ he writes about. Once he is caught up in his own adoration, he cannot seem to separate himself from worshipping. We join him at his own private altar and there, locked in a three-way mystery that flows between God, *The Via Advent,* and the reader, we are captured and forbidden to leave the presence of God. It is of no use to say, "Shut out some of the light; we are not used to such intensity, such radiance, such glory. He will have ultimate light or no light at all."

The Via Advent, like *The Via Crucis* before it, is an oasis for the soul. Advent, as powerful as Luke describes it, has risen again. Mary and Joseph have once more taken up residence in a stable. A baby has cried. We are free! Incarnation is the only miracle in which all others take root.

Calvin Miller
May 2010
www.calvinmillerauthor.com

After a fifteen year absence, I was back in the holy city of Jerusalem with a specific objective in mind. Just the day before, I had joined hundreds of Christian pilgrims from around the world in a slow amble through the labyrinth of the Old City on a route set by Franciscan monks hundreds of years ago. The Via Dolorosa, as it is commonly known, was a path I dreamed of walking for several years. My pack contained a manuscript of my soon-to-be released book, *The Via Crucis*.

I carried the manuscript to the church of the Holy Sepulcher in search of a blessing. An elderly Greek priest laid hands, seasoned by years of supplication, on the book while we stood in front of Christendom's most sacred spot: the Empty Tomb. It was a poetic finish to a writing journey that I had been on for years.

That evening, over a mouthwatering meal of hummus and strong Arabic tea, my traveling buddy Keith and I decided on an appropriate walk for the following day. Departing from the archaic Jaffa Gate that crisp November morning was quite a treat. Only a few miles south of Jerusalem, another town known around the world—Bethlehem, the City of Bread—was that day's destination. Leaving the hustle and bustle of the Jerusalem suburbs behind, we spent several pleasant hours in the unfilled spaces on the hills above the great valley that separates the two towns.

Passing through the secured border checkpoints into Palestinian territory meant entering a different world. We continued up the hillsides that lead into the heart of the busy town of Bethlehem, always with the great valley to our left. In those valleys two millennia ago, an angelic army burst through time and space announcing the Incarnation of the Great Shepherd to a company of terrified goat and sheep herders.

At the Church of the Nativity, which sits at the top of Bethlehem, I joined a multitude of Spanish pilgrims, in praise and adulation at the Holy Grotto, the celebrated birthplace of Jesus. As they worshiped the One who came as a gift for all mankind, in their native tongue, I quietly wept. That walk from Jerusalem to Bethlehem, undoubtedly taken a few times by the holy family when they found themselves citizens of Bethlehem for a short period of their lives, became the seedbed of my mind for the book you now hold in your hands.

How to Use This Book

The Via Advent is a part of the Via Series that chronicles the Christ-story. Its predecessor, *The Via Crucis,* began with the last thirty-six hours of the life of Christ and concluded with His triumphant resurrection. Though written as a Lenten devotional, thousands have read *The Via Crucis* throughout the year. *The Via Advent* is a forty-day devotional broken into four sections. Part I—The Seed introduces us to a fictional storyteller who explains how the promise of Messiah has been scattered like seeds throughout the history of the Hebrews. Part II—The End of Silence follows the dramatic and often humorous story of Zechariah and Elizabeth, the parents of the forerunner John the Baptist. Part III—The Advent unveils the dramatic and often nail-biting tale of the earthly parents of the God-Child. Part IV—The Epiphany is the essential element that brings this part of the story of Christ to a close. Unfortunately, much of the church today has lost the celebration of Epiphany, the twelve days following Christmas, which primarily conveys Christ's revealed glory through the story of the Magi who sought the God-Child.

If you use this book during the Advent season, it should be started on November 27. Part II—The End of the Silence, will begin December 1 with Chapter 5, Theophilus. Part III will end on Christmas Day with Chapter 29—Jesus. The final chapter of the book, aptly titled Epiphany, will end on January 6.

Each short chapter is written in four distinctive sections. The first page contains the beautiful art of Jenny Slaver illustrating the daily reading. Take a moment to contemplate the image before moving to the scriptures. Holy Scripture is written in chronological order to give more flow to the story. The next section is a tale taken from the perspective of one of the multitude of characters we meet on this journey. I am sure you will relate to a variety of responses you discover in those who were a part of the unfolding story. Bringing it all together are the prayers at the end of the chapters that clarify the focus of the individual story. Through the inspiration of Calvin Miller's *The Celtic Way of Prayer*, most of the prayers are Trinitarian—three stanzas always ending with "Blessed Trinity, help me to understand Your Advent." But throughout the book I have allowed several prayers to be inspired by beloved Christmas songs. I hope to revive a little inspiration in the reader for those songs of old. The Epiphany section has an additional component. Whenever you come to the stories of the Magi, I have inserted a stanza from *The Quest of the Magi* by John Hopkins Jr. in which I found much inspiration. When you have finished, I suggest you return to the image and take a concluding moment of contemplation.

My prayer is that you will experience the presence of Christ through this tiny book. To experience the Incarnate One is to never be content with the world that is. May this book help you to consider His initial coming and anticipate His coming again.

THE VIA ADVENT

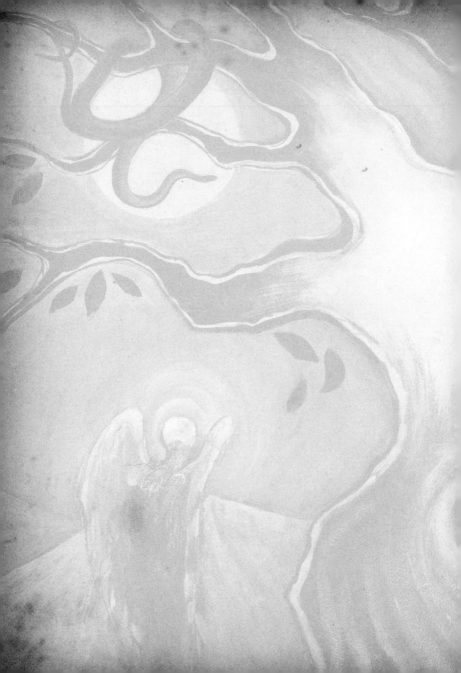

PART I
The Seed

The Word became a human
being and lived here with
us. We saw his true
glory, the glory of the only
Son of the Father. From
him all the kindness and all the
truth of God have come
down to us.

John 1:14 (CEV)

The Great Silence

Where myth and mystery became Man,
history stopped and once again, began.
Shawn Small

In the beginning was the one who is called the Word. The Word was with God and was truly God. From the very beginning the Word was with God. And with this Word, God created all things. Nothing was made without the Word. Everything that was created received its life from him, and his life gave light to everyone. The light keeps shining in the dark, and darkness has never put it out.
John 1:1–5 (CEV)

The Great Silence, as it came to be known among the heavenly citizens, had lasted for some four hundred years. The voice of God had not been uttered since the prophet Malachi. Throughout the years of silence, the chosen people moved from quiet concern over Yahweh's hush to agitated anxiety. Where were His prophets? Where was His voice? But as is the habit of human nature, the Jewish nation eventually settled into a religious routine to help soothe their aching fears of the silence. If the Almighty was not talking, if He had decided to stay far away, there was nothing they could do but hope and wait. One day, Messiah would return, as was promised throughout the Holy Writ. As the years passed like a melting storm, the Messianic promises became dust-covered myths and metaphors in the heart of the religious leadership. They were nothing more than whispered rumors amongst the common folk.

Eventually, another foreign menace invaded the Promised Land as Jewish leaders used their faith as arms to wage warfare against the pagan ways of the Roman oppressors. Soon the common men and women who were most affected by the abusive policies of their Roman overlords began to once again whisper about the promises of Messiah. They thought the Great Silence would eventually end with the return of the Lord Almighty. As with Babylon, Egypt, and Assyria, God would free His people from their oppressors with the fire of judgment.

One angel had been watching this tiny speck of Judean desert for eons with the anticipation of the ages. His name was Lucis, Heavenly Chronicler. Recording and telling the story of Yahweh was his entire reason for existence. The last few years had been quiet, but nothing ever remained still in the heavenly realms. The recent rumors of a pending holy invasion caused Lucis to feel as if he would burst like a supernova if it did not come soon.

As flying is to a bird, so eagerness was part of Lucis's nature. Sensing the vibrant approach of seraphim wings, Lucis grabbed his gear and stood with eager expectation. "Finally, the Advent is beginning."

Gabriel, the sentinel of God, could not help but smile as he approached the Chronicler. He immediately noticed that Lucis was wearing his satchel filled with an assortment of parchment and pens, awaiting his assignment from on High. "Is it time? Has the invasion begun?" Lucis fired forth his questions like a newly awakened cherub. Gabriel laid a strong hand upon Lucis's shoulder, and spoke. "Patience storyteller, the fullness of time is almost upon us but you must first be reminded of the foretelling of the Seed before this new tale unfolds."

Lucis spoke with slight embarrassment. "Yes, sir. I am sorry for my impatience. I have waited for this moment since the Terrible Rupture."

"We all have, Dear One. Steady up now for the Advent is at hand."

Time swirled around the angelic beings like a desert sand storm as they traveled back to that first promise of the Word's return, the Advent of the Ages.

Lord, there are times in my life when silence reigns
and the clamor of this world confounds my thoughts;
I long for Your voice; for the whisper of Messiah
and I ask, where is the Advent, the coming of the King?

In those moments of silence, my soul longs for You
like the desert deer longs for a life-giving oasis.
And I realize You never left. You were cultivating
my heart through my longing, through the silence.

Father, in the silence, remind me that You never forsake.
Son, in the silence, remind me the Word is never voiceless.
Spirit, in the silence, may You teach me to be still and know.
Blessed Trinity, help me understand Your Advent.

But when the
fullness
of the time came, God
sent forth His Son,
born of a woman,
born under the
Law.

Galatians 4:4 (NASB)

The Terrible Rupture

Of man's disobedience,
and the fruit of that forbidden tree
whose mortal taste brought death into all the world,
and all our woe.
John Milton, *Paradise Lost*

So the LORD God said to the snake: "Because of what you have done, you will be the only animal to suffer this curse—For as long as you live, you will crawl on your stomach and eat dirt. You and this woman will hate each other; your descendants and hers will always be enemies. One of hers will strike you on the head, and you will strike him on the heel."

Genesis 3:14–15 (CEV)

The swirl of epoch-dust started to slow as it revealed the angels' first stopover on their sojourn through time. Lucis was accustomed to traversing the universe at light speed and leaping throughout the heavenly realms without incident, but crossing time was a new adventure for him. It took him a moment to get his bearings. As their location became obvious, Lucis let out a startled gasp.

"We are moments before the Terrible Rupture!" he thought out loud. Gabriel acknowledged his assessment, and without moving his eyes away from the garden scene, he said, "Watch, young one. This was the beginning—the beginning of many promises, the Seed of the Advent." But in Lucis's mind this moment was the end of hope for mankind.

The Fallen One, gilded with serpentine beauty and a liquid tongue that poured both artificial praise and subtle deceptions, had spent months wooing the Woman away from the heart of the Creator with delicate whispers of deception that she ingested like a slow poison. Though administered in microscopic amounts, the ruse built to lethal levels in her heart. The angelic forces wanted to storm the Garden of Eden and rescue God's children, but the Voice that echoed in their spirits was firm: "They must choose. You must not interfere."

The instant the Woman partook of the fruit, Eden mourned. For although the Woman now possessed the full scope of the knowledge of good and evil, Eden had lost its mother. But when the Man willfully bit of the forbidden fruit, the Terrible Rupture of disobedience sent a spasm of searing agony across the universe. In that moment the blue orb started to lose its color and vibrancy. It was like watching a man's life drain from his body. "What was" became "what could have been." Lucis wanted to close his eyes. The pain of watching the Terrible Rupture for a second time seemed too much. Why were they here?

As their Father entered the garden, as He did every day at this time, what once was a moment of reverence and excitement amongst His children had distorted into malignant fear. Lucis watched as the Father's heart broke in the choices of His children. The Man's decision had twisted the universe.

Lucis witnessed the judgment of the Fallen One then heard the Father's words in a way he had not perceived the first time: *You and this woman will hate each other; your descendants and hers will always be enemies. One of hers will strike you on the head, and you will strike him on the heel.* The word "One" reverberated in Lucis's spirit over and over again. He did not know why, but he pulled out a scroll and wrote down "One of hers." What did that mean and why did he not catch that the first time he witnessed the Terrible Rupture. Who was this One?

Gabriel looked on as Lucis repeatedly wrote the statement along with a multitude of questions that were invading his spirit. Seeing Gabriel out of the corner of his eye, Lucis stopped writing and slowly rolled up the parchment and returned it to his satchel. "This was the first of the promises, the Seed of Advent. Hold on now, for we have much to cover and the hour grows short."

How many times have I fallen after
listening to the poisoned tongue of the enemy of God?
The Terrible Rupture occurs in my heart
each time I turn from Your voice.

How I long for freedom from this battle
and obedience to Thy will instead of my will.
Then I remember Your abundant promises and
the blood You shed to forgive all my sins.

For the Father who sent the Son.
For the Son who fulfilled the will of the Father.
For the Spirit who assures us of our forgiveness.
Blessed Trinity, help me understand Your Advent.

And in your Seed [Christ] shall all the nations of the earth be blessed and [by Him] bless themselves, because you have heard and obeyed My voice.

Genesis 22:18 (AMP)

Seeds

A wonderful stream is the River Time,
As it runs through the realm of Tears,
With a faultless rhythm, and a musical rhyme,
A broader sweep, a surge sublime,
As it blends with the Ocean of Years.
Benjamin Franklin Taylor, from "The River Time"

Behold, the days are coming, declares the LORD, when I will raise up for David a righteous Branch, and he shall reign as king and deal wisely, and shall execute justice and righteousness in the land. In his days Judah will be saved, and Israel will dwell securely. And this is the name by which he will be called: "The LORD is our righteousness."
Jeremiah 23:5–6 (ESV)

In preparation for Lucis's assignment, Gabriel traveled through time with him to witness the key moments of promise made to the chosen people throughout their brief history on the blue orb. Lucis found these abrupt stops in history uncomfortably jarring, but his pen and parchment never left his hand. Each transition went from a blurred, distorted mix of colors and lights to a slow focus on a new moment in time. It was as if Lucis was watching raining paint slowly forming a complete image on a blank canvas.

At this moment the angels hovered as the world slowly came into view. They were hanging over a small mountain. Below them, the patriarch Abraham stood frozen with a glinting sacrificial knife in his upraised hand. This was the very knife he had used before the call of Yahweh. His son, Isaac, the child of promise, was tied beneath Abraham like a lamb at the slaughter. Isaac trembled, his eyes closed tightly, as he lay on the makeshift altar as a willing sacrifice. After a burst of holy light, Lucis saw Abraham look to the left, surprised by a visitor. With great relief to Lucis, even though he already knew the tale, the knife fell from the patriarch's hands. As the words slowly became audible, Lucis witnessed the sobbing forms of the father and son of Israel, holding each other in a thankful embrace. One of their angelic companions stood at Abraham's side, seemingly unaware of his hovering observers overhead. The angel spoke of blessings and obedience, of descendants like the stars of the sky and the sand of the seashore. He then spoke the words Lucis was compelled to record: *And your Seed will possess all that the enemy has stolen. And through your Seed all nations, all peoples of the earth will blessed.* Lucis started to write of the Seed and he was once again pulled away.

Lucis feverishly copied down the words of Israel's greatest figures as Gabriel pulled him through time. They rushed toward a massive palace built of cedar on the hills of Salem. The majestic King David was on his knees with head bowed as the prophet Nathan declared, *When your days are over and you rest with your fathers, I will raise up One to succeed you, who will come from your lineage, and I will establish His kingdom. He is the One who will build a house for my Name, and I will establish the throne of His kingdom forever.*

Another blur, then Lucis found they were standing at the end of the aqueduct on the Upper Pool of Jerusalem, a city now surrounded by an invading enemy. He could hear hundreds of the enemies' banners outside of the city, snapping in the wind like the cracking scourges that would soon be upon their backs. The overpowering smell of the unburied dead filled his nostrils. The prophet Isaiah was in the midst of a powerful confrontation with a desperate King Ahaz. *You doubt? The Lord Himself will give a sign to this stubborn people. Look! A virgin will conceive a child! She will give birth to a son and will call Him Immanuel, God is among us.* Lucis struggled to record the information that now filled his spirit. With the swirling of epoch-dust came another king, another prophet, another age: *The time is coming, through My decree, when I will plant a truly righteous Seed from David; a ruler who understands justice and One that will draw My people into unity. In his age, Judah will once again be secure and Israel will live in peace. And His name shall be God-Who-Is-Justice.*

Though Lucis could not see Gabriel in the transitions, he heard his whisper, "Continued patience child. Just a few more promises of the Advent."

I remember the promises of God
given to Abraham for his willing obedience.
I remember the promises of God
given to David as he sought God with his whole heart.

I remember the promises of God
given to Isaiah as he faithfully spoke God's word.
I remember the promises of God
given to Jeremiah even though his heart was breaking.

Father, You are the Promise-Giver.
Son, You are the Promise-Keeper.
Spirit, You are the Promise-Reminder.
Blessed Trinity, help me understand Your Advent.

Yes, Messenger of the Covenant, the one you've been waiting for. Look! He's on his way!

Malachai 3:1b (THE MESSAGE)

Before the Silence IV

He (God) sent the human race what I call good dreams: I mean those
queer stories scattered all through the heathen religions about a god
who dies and comes to life again and, by his death, has somehow given
new life to men.

C. S. Lewis, *The Case for Christianity*

But you, Bethlehem, David's country, the runt of the litter—From you
will come the leader who will shepherd-rule Israel. He'll be no upstart,
no pretender. His family tree is ancient and distinguished. Meanwhile,
Israel will be in foster homes until the birth pangs are over and the
child is born, And the scattered brothers come back home to the family
of Israel. He will stand tall in his shepherd-rule by God's strength,
centered in the majesty of God-Revealed. And the people will have a
good and safe home, for the whole world will hold him in respect—
Peacemaker of the world!

Micah 5: 2–4 (THE MESSAGE)

Micah scribed the thoughts that divinely flooded his mind. Lucis found himself materializing over the young prophet's shoulder as he wrote down the words upon the vellum scroll. Some of the expressions seemed to glow on the parchment: *But you, Bethlehem Ephratah, though you are tiny amongst the clans of Judah; yet out of you shall One emerge the ruler of Israel, whose coming forth has been from ancient days. Therefore he shall give them up until the time when she who is in labor has given birth.* As they faded back into the epoch-dust, Lucis realized that these were the clues that would solve deep mysteries slowly unfolding in his spirit.

Now their journey headed in a very different direction as Gabriel took Lucis to tribes scattered across the blue orb. As they visited the people, Lucis noticed how humanity had traveled on jagged paths as they moved away from Eden. Lucis found their endless attempts to create bridges to God through their countless religious practices both humorous and heartbreaking. Did they not realize they would never be able to find God in their wisdom and through their rituals? If only they understood that the Creator must find them. As he looked deeper, he began to comprehend that the ancient stories of Jehovah were sown deep in the collective consciousness of each tribe's assorted beliefs. There were seeds of truth, sometimes microscopic, in their tribal practices. He barely had time to write, "Eternity is truly set in the hearts of all men . . ." before he was yanked away once again.

They now hung in the heavens above the earth. As they hovered above the miracle of creation, Gabriel allowed Lucis to stare deeply into the beauty of God's handiwork. On the surface of the planet there was the great panorama of sweeping deserts, majestic seas, and profuse jungles. The wonder and beauty of the animal kingdom enthralled Lucis, and the plant life was as varied as the stars in the sky. "Now Lucis, look deeper into the heart of creation." His vision was taken beyond the visual and into the internal web of life that held ecosystems in place. Beyond the splendor and under the complexity of creation he saw something quite unexpected. He could not decide if this emotion was angst or anticipation. He opened his scroll and wrote: "It is hard for me to believe, but even creation anxiously awaits and longs for the revealing of the Son. The blue orb cries out for a Savior, a Seed that would reverse the effects of the Terrible Rupture."

Gabriel turned toward Lucis and spoke as one finishing a fruitful but exhausting journey, "There is one last picture you must see before you begin to record the tale of the Advent. We now must visit the last prophet before the Great Silence as he foretells of the first prophet of the age of Advent." Then the pair came upon Malachi as he spoke the words of God to an unhearing religious leadership some one hundred years following their captivity by the Babylonians, "Look! I am sending my messenger on ahead to clear the way for me. Suddenly the One you have been looking for will enter His Temple—yes, Messiah of the Covenant, the One you've been waiting for. Look! He's on the way! Listen to the mouth of the Lord of the Angelic-Hosts."

Then the voyage was finished. Lucis was back in the present. How would he catalog all he had witnessed on his journey across time and space? Though Gabriel was no longer with him, Lucis heard a voice in his spirit: "You are now to be present at the Advent and record all you witness. The story begins in the quiet hills outside Jerusalem. . . ."

I take this moment to step back, acknowledging
how often You reached out to me when I was lost.
Through the lives of those who sincerely follow You.
Through the Word of God that utters Your Voice.

Through the conviction of my sins
and a mind that asks questions about life.
For the wonders of creation that echoes Your Presence
and the still small voice that caught me off guard.

Father, You called me.
Son, You came for me.
Spirit, You led me.
Blessed Trinity, help me understand Your Advent.

PART II
The End
of the Silence

I know that you heard about him, and you are in him, so you were taught the truth that is in Jesus.

Ephesians 4:21 (NCV)

Theophilus

"I am of your opinion," said Sampson, "but it is one thing to write like a poet, and another thing to write like a historian. The poet can tell or sing of things, not as they were but as they ought to have been, whereas the historian must describe them, not as they ought to have been but as they were, without exaggerating or suppressing the truth in any particular."

Miguel de Cervantes, *Don Quixote* (Part II, Chapter 3)

So many others have tried their hand at putting together a story of the wonderful harvest of Scripture and history that took place among us, using reports handed down by the original eyewitnesses who served this Word with their very lives. Since I have investigated all the reports in close detail, starting from the story's beginning, I decided to write it all out for you, most honorable Theophilus, so you can know beyond the shadow of a doubt the reliability of what you were taught.

Luke 1:1–4 (The Message)

The physician, as he was called by his closest friends, was seated at his writing table in what an outside observer may have thought a catatonic state. He had been in silent prayer for a long time. Several years earlier, when the idea for the correspondence first came to his mind, he merely thought it a good idea. He would compose a simple letter of encouragement to his dear friend Theophilus. They had grown up together in the Syriac town of Antioch. Both came from privileged families affording them the best educations that the Roman Empire offered. Though their education paths would diverge as Luke pursued medicine and Theophilus focused on philosophy, rhetoric, and Roman law, their friendship never waned. Even in this hallowed moment Luke smiled at the debates they once had about an eccentric Jew named Saul of Tarsus who had a fantastic religious conversion very near their town. In a few short years, Saul would change his name to Paul and he would turn the Empire upside down. As gentiles, Luke and Theophilus found the whole notion of Judaism and the new cult of Christians philosophically interesting at best. That was until Luke met Paul while he was on a trip to Troas.

Luke the gentile, the doctor, the historian, the skeptic, the humanist became Luke the follower of Christ and co-laborer of Paul. For the next several years, he traveled with the apostle experiencing things he could not explain in scientific terms. The one person he most desired to share his story with was Theophilus, now a high ranking Roman official. But he thought Luke had become as foolish as Paul the preacher. Why would his friend give up a brilliant career in medicine to chase after Saul based on the urging of an invisible man named Jesus?

Like any historian worth his academic credentials, Luke began to compile the specifics that surrounded the story of Jesus of Nazareth. He had personally gathered reports from a multitude of eyewitnesses. The years he spent interviewing Paul, a brilliant academic himself, opened up his mind to the complexities and beauty of Judaism. Luke observed the sweeping cross-cultural effect this gospel had on tribes from every culture it encountered. He carefully researched the Jewish story and the precise historical and unbiased facts of living history that were readily available. All said, Luke had compiled an impressive life-account of the Savior.

To his great delight, his prayers had been answered before the final draft of his discourse was composed. In a letter to Luke, Theophilus wrote that he had become a follower of the same Christ that Luke proclaimed so freely. Since the name Theophilus meant lover of God, Luke felt that it was providentially given to him before any of his gentile family knew the God of love who sought to water their thirsty souls.

The physician opened his eyes and picked up his quill. The story must begin at the Advent, the birth of Jesus. His composition would now be a letter of encouragement rather than one of persuasion. Putting pen to page, he began: *So many others have tried their hand at putting together a story of the wonderful harvest of Scripture and history that took place among us, using reports handed down by the original eyewitnesses who served this Word with their very lives. Since I have investigated all the reports in close detail, starting from the story's beginning, I decided to write it all out for you, most honorable Theophilus, so you can know beyond the shadow of a doubt the reliability of what you were taught.*

Amazing grace, how sweet the sound
that saved a wretch like me.
How do I share that amazing grace
with those around me who so desperately need it?

I pray for (insert name) who needs Your strength.
I pray for (insert name) who needs Your peace.
I pray for (insert name) who needs Your joy.
I pray for (insert name) who needs Your forgiveness.

It is the Father who hears and answers our prayers.
It is the Son who hears and answers our prayers.
It is the Spirit who hears and answers our prayers.
Blessed Trinity, help me understand Your Advent.

I will make rivers flow
on barren heights, and
springs within the valleys.
I will turn the desert
into pools of water,
and the parched ground
into springs.

Isaiah 41:18 (NIV)

Barren

Repeating the prayer again and again he tried wildly to distract his attention; but the prayer could not tranquillize his agonized heart. "Lord, why are you silent? Why are you always silent?"

Shusaku Endo, *Silence*

During the rule of Herod, King of Judea, there was a priest assigned service in the regiment of Abijah. His name was Zachariah. His wife was descended from the daughters of Aaron. Her name was Elizabeth. Together they lived honorably before God, careful in keeping to the ways of the commandments and enjoying a clear conscience before God. But they were childless because Elizabeth could never conceive, and now they were quite old.

Luke 1:5–7 (THE MESSAGE)

There had been no words between them as they slowly paced through the tiny village streets, arm in arm, on their way home from the synagogue. The village was alive with bustling families returning from the morning's worship to an afternoon of tasty food, a Sabbath's rest, and the loving laughter of children. Yet, their home would be as it always was: silent. The visiting Rabbi's teaching about the matriarch Sarah's infertility and God's miraculous gift of Isaac should have brought hope and faith to the barren couple. Instead, it brought only painful echoes to two old and empty hearts.

Many years ago, before either one could walk, their parents promised them to each other. Both came from blessed bloodlines. Elizabeth was of priestly descent and Zachariah was born into the division of Abijah. They fell in love during their year of engagement and once they were given in covenant to each other, they flourished. Zachariah loved his priestly duties and Elizabeth kept firm order in the household. She considered making the often serious and talkative Zachariah smile as her primary calling. Her husband could be so solemn when he focused on his piety or when he came home after a tough week at the Temple. She knew his mood the moment he walked in by the stoic horizontal lips that secured themselves to his face, daring her to try to move them. But she always could make him break into a grin. If especially desperate, there was always the hidden tickle spot on his elbow. After she declared victory in her quest she would remind Zachariah, "Think how wonderful it will be when the laughter of children fills this home." He would often hold her (she could still feel the laughter heaving in his chest) and say, "Elizabeth, there will be more laughter from little ones than we can imagine."

But it never happened. The years ticked on and the couple tried, but Elizabeth never conceived. Growing embarrassment overshadowed the couple whenever a new child was born in the village. Prayers of desperation eventually followed and their family wondered if children would ever arrive. The inevitable questions were asked: Did we sin against the Almighty? What have we done wrong? Why is God silent to our prayers? Eventually, they just hid their questions, doubt, and disappointment in the back of their minds like dust under an old, unmoved rug.

The Rabbi's teaching this Sabbath day reopened the wounds like grave robbers opening an old tomb in the middle of the night. Zachariah thought about the interpretation of their names. Zachariah meant "Jehovah has Remembered" and Elizabeth translated to "God is my Promise." Yet, Jehovah did not remember and apparently His promises were saved for only those blessed by His providence. They sat together as they did at the end of every Sabbath day. They held worn hands aged by hard work, and they prayed. "Lord, we do not understand and that is alright. We know You love us and though we are beyond the years of childbearing we trust Your will. In Your love we rest. We are Your children and that is enough."

What they did not see was the invisible angelic being that stood smiling, watching them just beyond the barrier of their world. "My friends, you are about to get more than you could ever imagine."

I have felt the pangs of bareness
when my prayers remained unanswered.
When I ask the desperate questions,
they seem to fall on deaf ears. Where have I sinned?

Why is God silent to my prayers?
Then doubt and disappointment become my companions.
But I must remember that I do not have to understand
because Your love is sufficient. In that love I rest.

May the Father shield me.
May the Son keep me.
May the Spirit fill me.
Blessed Trinity, help me understand Your Advent.

The Messenger-Angel again called me to attention. It was like being wakened out of deep sleep.

Zechariah 4:1 (THE MESSAGE)

Chosen Lot

I shall never believe that God plays dice with the world.
Albert Einstein

It so happened that as Zachariah was carrying out his priestly duties before God, working the shift assigned to his regiment, it came his one turn in life to enter the sanctuary of God and burn incense. The congregation was gathered and praying outside the Temple at the hour of the incense offering. Unannounced, an angel of God appeared just to the right of the altar of incense. Zachariah was paralyzed in fear.
Luke 1:8–12 (THE MESSAGE)

Zachariah could scarcely believe the crowds that had gathered in the Outer Courts of the Temple. Today was not a high holy day nor was there any impending tragedy or political problem. But for some reason the people gathered en masse, awaiting morning prayers in the Outer Courts of the Temple. The sight of hundreds of faithful Jews praying was always inspiring to Zachariah, but today the crowds made him nervous and on edge. "Stage fright," he thought. "It's just a bit of the jitters. That is to be expected."

From the time of King David, the Levite priests had been divided into twenty-four groups that would take turns in the daily priestly duties. The division of Abijah had been serving for the past week, as they did twice a year. The greatest honor a priest could experience was to go before the altar of incense in the Holy Place to add the sacred spice and render prayers before the Almighty for the children of Israel. This happened once every morning and evening. Tradition dictated that the one selected for the blessed responsibility was chosen by lot. Those outside of the Levitical tribes could only guess at what the lots were. Some argued that it was the drawing of straws while others were convinced it was the tossing of dice. What no one argued about, however, was that the outcome of the toss was orchestrated by God. This morning's lot fell to Zachariah. He could not believe it. He was almost fifty, the age of retirement from his Levitical duties. He had given up hope of ever being chosen by lot. As he put on his vestments for the honored occasion, his superior spoke, "Zachariah, you have waited many years to enter the Holy Place. Do not be nervous, but rejoice that you have been chosen by God!"

The petitioning crowd parted as Zachariah slowly hobbled through. He took in each sight and sound like the fleeting scent of a fresh cut rose. His walking stick kept his uneasy steps stable. At this moment, he was the focal point of the entire Jewish nation. Moving from the Outer Courts and into the Holy Place he came before the brazen altar, where incense had continually burned for hundreds of years. Walking toward the fire, he first noticed the blood of sacrifice sprinkled on the horns of the altar. Edging closer he saw the golden orange coals that hungrily awaited the sacred spices. He observed the thick curtain that separated him from the Holy of Holies, the very Presence of Yahweh. Apart from the High Priest entering the Holy of

Holies, this was the closest any man could come to God's presence. At this moment that man was Zachariah.

With the tenderness of a father holding his newborn child, Zachariah began to poor the precious mixture of spices onto the altar. As the sacred flame consumed the singular mixture of frankincense, onycha, stacte, and galbanum, an aroma burst forward unlike any other in the world for this was the only place that this mixture was ever used. The sacred scent enveloped Zachariah in a fog. This was the fragrance that Moses declared pleasing to the Lord.

He remembered that at this very moment countless other burnt offerings were being given for the people. With eyes closed, Zachariah came to himself as he began to pray for Israel. The aroma was the symbol of his prayers, the petitions of the hundreds gathered in the Outer Courts and thousands throughout the Promised Land. He continued for several minutes ending his prayer by asking for the return of the Messiah. But before he finished he asked one last thing: "God, why did you not give me an heir?"

A sudden rush of otherworldly atmosphere caused Zachariah to stand paralyzed with fear. He did not want to open his eyes but when he did he saw a very large figure standing opposite him, on the other side of the altar. All that came out of Zachariah's mouth were the words, "Father, please spare my life."

I stand in the Temple longing for Your Presence
clothed in the righteousness won by the Son.
I move forward into the Outer Courts
as I pray for Your will to be done.

I enter the Inner Courts with praise on my lips,
to the Holy of Holies where Your Presence dwells.
There I find my voice ceases at the wonder
that You allow me into the very Throne Room of God.

I stand before the Father who created me.
I stand before the Son who purchased me.
I stand before the Spirit that cleansed me.
Blessed Trinity, help me understand Your Advent.

I the Lord
All-Powerful,
will send my messenger
to prepare the way
for me.

Malachi 3:1a (CEV)

An Unexpected Response

'Tis strange–but true;
for truth is always strange;
Stranger than fiction.
Lord Byron, *Don Juan*

But the angel said to him, *"Do not be afraid, Zechariah, for your
prayer has been heard, and your wife Elizabeth will bear you a son,
and you shall call his name John. And you will have joy and gladness,
and many will rejoice at his birth, for he will be great before the Lord.
And he must not drink wine or strong drink, and he will be filled with
the Holy Spirit, even from his mother's womb. And he will turn many
of the children of Israel to the Lord their God, and he will go before
him in the spirit and power of Elijah, to turn the hearts of the fathers
to the children, and the disobedient to the wisdom of the just, to make
ready for the Lord a people prepared."*
Luke 1:13–17 (ESV)

Why do they always look as if they will die?" thought an amused Gabriel who had been waiting next to the altar of incense before Zachariah had even entered the Holy Place. "If only they understood that one day they will be judges of our species." Standing an angelic arms length away from the man frozen in a seizure of terror, Gabriel remembered the time he appeared to the prophet Daniel to help him interpret the vision of the Lord and how he had to pick that terrified man of God up off of the ground as he grasped the muddy banks of the Ulai River. "If only Zachariah realized the part he will play in the Messiah's coming. I should be the one who trembles at the way the Master indwells his children."

Gabriel had been blessed to be the mouthpiece of God unto mankind throughout history. Announcing the coming of the Messiah was his primary purpose for existence. As the Lord opened Zachariah's eyes to the archangel's presence, Gabriel knew his first words would be the same as they always were when humans and angels met face to face.

"Do not fear, Zachariah." It was not the words that eased Zachariah's fear but the smile that came upon Gabriel's lips. "Your prayer has been heard. Elizabeth, your wife, will bear a son by you." The look of fear was replaced by a look Gabriel could only describe as comical astonishment. "You are to name him John. You're going to leap like a gazelle for joy." Zachariah thought about how he had hobbled through the crowd into the Holy Place. "And not only you—many will rejoice greatly in his birth. He'll be great and distinguished in God's sight." Gabriel carefully stopped to study the man's face. His initial fear seemed to have been replaced with uneasiness, not of a man being confronted by a heavenly being, but one who was somehow the victim of a universal prank.

Gabriel, unfazed by Zachariah's reaction to the good news, continued his proclamation. "He must never taste alcohol and he'll be filled and directed by the Holy Spirit from the moment he leaves his mother's womb." Zachariah could not get beyond the words "the moment he leaves his mother's womb." Did this angel not understand that his wife's womb was unable to bear a child? The mighty Gabriel continued. His voice was growing in resonance as his excitement of the proclamation built to a crescendo. "He will turn many of the lost sons and daughters of Israel back to the Lord their God. He will herald God's arrival in the style and strength of Elijah. He will go before the One in the spirit and power of Elijah, turning back the hearts of the parents to the children, and kindling devout understanding among hardened skeptics—he'll get the people ready for God." These were the words, spoken and written in the Holy Writ before the Great Silence.

The promise would be fulfilled.

Gabriel stood, radiant in the words of the Spirit that spoke through him. What would Zachariah's response be to the first spoken words of God since the Great Silence? Working up the courage Zachariah spoke, "Sir, I have a question."

Lord, I come before you with the desires of my heart.
Jesus, you said that I can ask anything in
Your name and You will give it to me
if I love You with my whole heart and obey Your commands.

Teach me to be a person who fearlessly obeys Your voice.
Teach me to be a person who passionately loves You.
Teach me to ask only those things that are of Your will
and have the courage to live out the answers to my prayers.

May the Father be my master.
May the Son be my shepherd.
May the Spirit be my guardian.
Blessed Trinity, help me understand Your Advent.

While I was **absorbed** in this **praying**, the humanlike **Gabriel**, the one I had **seen** in an earlier vision, approached me.

Daniel 9:21b (THE MESSAGE)

Muted Doubt

IX

> *Wonder rather than doubt*
> *is the root of all knowledge.*
> **Abraham Joshua Heschel**

And Zechariah said to the angel, "How shall I know this? For I am an old man, and my wife is advanced in years." And the angel answered him, "I am Gabriel. I stand in the presence of God, and I was sent to speak to you and to bring you this good news. And behold, you will be silent and unable to speak until the day that these things take place, because you did not believe my words, which will be fulfilled in their time."

Luke 1:18–20 (ESV)

The irony of the moment was not lost to the archangel. Here, before the Holy of Holies, the very presence of God, the man of God stood, the closest he would ever come in his lifetime to the Tabernacle. He encounters the Messenger-Angel bearing the most miraculous news from on High that any man could ever imagine. His impossible prayer, the petition that he carried upon his lips for decades, would be answered! God has heard his prayer and his home would finally be filled with the laughter of a son. Not only would Elizabeth bear a child, but this boy would be the forerunner to the Messiah! Every tribe in every nation would be blessed by John's life. The Great Silence was over.

And how did the righteous Zachariah greet this pronouncement? "Sir, I have a question. Do you expect me to believe this? I'm an old man and my wife is an old woman."

Gabriel was stunned at the man's desperate skepticism.

There is often a sea of doubt that rages deep beneath the surface of the life of even the most faithful. Years of unanswered prayers, the inward scarring of unjustified pains, and hidden struggles with sins that seem to so easily overcome us are hidden away and masked by our religious rituals, good deeds, and outward proclamations. While a sea of emotion, like a growing tsunami, rolls the keel of our heart, we fight to pretend that nothing is wrong. But a moment eventually arises where the façade is washed away and our true feelings, the ones we have avoided for years, come exploding to the surface of our lives. Usually, this happens in a moment of profound loss. For Zachariah, it was surfacing in his moment of wonder. A confrontation with the Spirit of Truth was too much for Zachariah and the deep doubts of his heart were suddenly revealed by the One who already knew how Zachariah felt. His hidden pains far outweighed his ability to trust in the God of his youth. But all of that was about to change.

Gabriel looked at Zachariah. The angelic smile had been replaced with a stern brow, "I am Gabriel, the sentinel of God, sent especially to bring you this abundantly good news. But because you won't believe me, you'll be unable to say a word until the day of your son's birth. Every word I've spoken to you will come true in God's time."

Zachariah tried, once again, to protest with his doubt but nothing came. His words were as empty as a well during drought. He went to scream in terror but all that burst forth from his mouth was a rush of silent breath.

Gabriel, Messenger of the Holy One, was gone. Zachariah stood alone and mute—now a sign of his doubt and God's promise.

Lord, there is often a sea of doubt
that rages deep beneath the surface of my life.
Unanswered prayers, pain, and hidden sins
are too easily masked by my shallow spirituality.

Lord, I am ready for the façade to be washed away.
I need an encounter with the Spirit of Truth
to reveal the reality of my heart's condition
that I may be set free to trust Your word and Your will.

Help me, Father, to mute the doubt in my heart.
Help me, Son of God, to release my pain to You.
Lead me, Spirit, to a life of freedom and joy.
Blessed Trinity, help me understand Your Advent.

Then the LORD said to Him, "Who has made man's mouth? Who makes him mute, or deaf, or seeing, or blind? Is it not I, the LORD?"

Exodus 4:11 (ESV)

Silent Visionary

*God is not so cruel as to give me a vision
in which there is no fulfillment.*
B. A. Bosworth

*Meanwhile, the congregation waiting for Zachariah was getting rest-
less, wondering what was keeping him so long in the sanctuary. When
he came out and couldn't speak, they knew he had seen a vision. He
continued speechless and had to use sign language with the people.
When the course of his priestly assignment was completed, he went
back home.*

Luke 1:21–23 (THE MESSAGE)

The unusually large crowds had grown restless over the last hour. It all started with a strange presence that swept over the multitude. Prayers, quite suddenly, shifted from whispered petitions pouring forth from the lips of hundreds to a sudden silence. Imagine the buzzing of thousand of locusts suddenly swept away by the wind. It was a presence that fell upon the assembly like a heavy wet cloak. No one dared ask but all wondered if this was the presence of the God of Abraham, Isaac, and Jacob. A reverence now stood guard in the Outer Courts causing the people to pray through the gentle swaying of their bodies back and forth as if their movements were delicately pushing their now unspoken prayers forward into the Holy of Holies.

After a few minutes, the presence lifted but the reverence continued for over an hour. The hush was slowly broken by a murmur of questions throughout the crowd. "Where is the priest? He should have been out quite a while ago." "Could it be possible what was said of old? Did the presence of God meet him?" "Did he peek behind the curtain into the Holy of Holies and now lay dead on the floor?" The longer Zachariah failed to appear, the louder the crowd grew and the wilder the rumors became. But the fear of God had remained and not a single Levite was willing to check on the tardy priest.

For a second time the crowd was silenced as the curtain opened and Zachariah came out of the Holy Place. It was not his emergence from the curtain but the look on Zachariah's face that hushed the assembly. As it was for Moses coming down the mountain, it was now for Zachariah. His face blazed with the presence of God. A luminous glow slowly drained from his appearance like a flame newly extinguished for lack of oxygen. His superior quickly ran to him saying, "Zachariah, what has happened?" But all he could do was hold his throat with one hand and sign with the other that he had no voice.

So used to expressing himself with words, Zachariah quickly grew frustrated in his attempt to communicate. He was forced to slow down and think of what he needed to say. He must share as concisely as possible. His normally busy tongue was bridled. The crowds surrounded him so closely that he could barely use his arms which were now a necessary component to his communication. Though it took several minutes, he finally explained to the crowd that he had seen a vision. Because of their experience in the Outer Courts, most believed something had happened but it would be up for debate for months to come what exactly "a vision" was.

The remainder of the week was blessedly normal. Zachariah's encounter and his sudden muteness kept most of his fellow priests at a distance. They often stared at him not knowing how to react or what to say. This did not matter to Zachariah whose mind was completely preoccupied with returning home. When the division of Abijah was finished with its duties, Zachariah quickly packed and headed to his village in the Judean hill country. He had much to tell Elizabeth and just a few hours to figure out how exactly to accomplish that task.

It was not until he was a few miles outside of Jerusalem that he realized he was no longer using a walking stick. He continued with a little hop in his step just like he had in his younger years.

More times than naught, Lord,
I find my mouth moving ahead of my mind.
Words that fall from my lips like daggers.
Words that hurt and confuse, that mean nothing.

I need Your wisdom, Lord,
to mute these loose lips
until You are the Lord of my voice.
So my words bring healing and peace.

Father, You gave me a voice.
And Son of God, You are the Word.
So Spirit, I surrender my lips to Your service.
Blessed Trinity, help me understand Your Advent.

God has made me laugh.
Now everyone will
laugh with me. Who would have
dared to tell Abraham
that someday I would have a child?
But in his old age,
I have given him a son.

Genesis 21:6-7 (CEV)

Elizabeth

XI

*I believe laughter
is a language of God.*
Yakov Smirnoff

*When the course of his priestly assignment was completed, he went
back home. It wasn't long before his wife, Elizabeth, conceived. She
went off by herself for five months, relishing her pregnancy. "So, this is
how God acts to remedy my unfortunate condition!" she said.*
Luke 1:23–25 (THE MESSAGE)

Elizabeth packed with ease. She did not need much for the journey back home. Laughing to herself, she stopped and stroked her fingers across her swollen belly. Young John, almost five months in the womb, was kicking again. "You are an active child, little one." She began to laugh as she regularly did these last few months. John kicked as if her mirth tickled him. Five months was a long time to be away from home and her beloved Zachariah, but she had enjoyed the seclusion as her womb ripened with the miracle child.

She thought back to the day Zachariah returned to their village after his prescribed week of service in Jerusalem. The rumors had traveled to her town two days before her husband arrived. There had been an incident in the Temple. One of the priests supposedly had a vision from God while serving at the altar of incense. Oh, how her husband had patiently waited for years to be chosen for the task, but alas, he would probably never get the chance. Nevertheless, her talkative mate was sure to bring home the news of God's broken silence. Not since the prophet Malachi had a word from God been uttered in Israel. She hoped and prayed that the rumors proved true.

She had been waiting, as she had twice a year throughout the last twenty five years of marriage, at the gates of their small town on the day she knew he would arrive. While filling the morning with the older women and their harmless local gossip, Elizabeth watched the arrival of a small Egyptian caravan carrying exotic goods. "That will add a bit of excitement in today's market," thought Elizabeth. It was silly but she was always nervous on his arrival day, as nervous as she had been on their wedding day. Shortly after noon she saw him crest the bend in the hill, traveling with several other priests in his order. When Zachariah saw Elizabeth at the gate he broke into a run, quickly leaving the others behind. "Where is his walking stick?" thought Elizabeth. The miracle sprint was the first of many surprises. Upon reaching her, he scooped her slightly plump frame off the ground and swung her around like he had when they were newlyweds. Then, without any shame, and in the sight of the town elders and the gathering marketers, he kissed her passionately. She tried to talk but all he did was place his finger over her lips to silence the questions that were filling her mind like a sudden flash flood. He swept her back to their home and loved her like it was their wedding night. Where did he get his energy? What happened in Jerusalem? Who was this man?

Later that evening, he would, through sign language and written words explain the Temple miracle and everything the archangel had spoken to him. Though it seemed absolutely outrageous, Elizabeth believed his story. That is when the laughter first began. Daily she would find herself doubled over with joyous belly laughs at God's sense of humor. "So, this is how God decides to remedy my unfortunate condition!"

Within a month, Elizabeth had known without a doubt that she was pregnant. Feeling the need to think through the situation and remain quiet about the details of the miracle, the couple decided she should go to a quiet family home on the border of Israel. There, she could contemplate and relish the season of pregnancy she had given up on ever enjoying. Now, five months later, Elizabeth was still laughing and could no longer wait to rejoin her voiceless husband back at home. "What will the neighbors think?" All she could do was let out a joy-filled burst of laughter.

There are so many desires and dreams
the Spirit has planted within my heart.
Ideas and requests that could only be birthed
by the planting of a divine seed.

All You want is me to seek the Kingdom of God
with all my heart, my soul, and my strength.
And those desires planted by God's Spirit
will spring up even if the ground looks barren.

In the name of the Father,
in the name of the Son,
in the name of the Spirit; Three in One.
Blessed Trinity, help me understand Your Advent.

PART III
The Advent

The birth of Jesus
took place like this.
His mother, Mary,
was engaged
to be married
to Joseph.

Matthew 1:18a (THE MESSAGE)

Joseph

For it is nothing other than love, Holy and chaste, full of sweetness and delight, love utterly serene and true, mutual and deep, which joins two beings, not in one flesh, but in one spirit, making them no longer two but one.

St. Bernard of Clairvaux

Hallelujah! The Master reigns, our God, the Sovereign-Strong! Let us celebrate, let us rejoice, let us give him the glory! The Marriage of the Lamb has come; his Wife has made herself ready. She was given a bridal gown of bright and shining linen. The linen is the righteousness of the saints.

Revelation 19:6 (THE MESSAGE)

Carving the finishing touches into the olive wood chest, a marriage gift for his soon-to-be bride, Joseph leaned back to admire the subtle craftsmanship he had etched into the beautiful piece of furniture. Smoothed edges and Hebrew lettering were considered excessive to most, but to Joseph they were small symbols of his love. He stood up looking around the bridal chamber that would soon be occupied by the blissful couple. He had insisted on building the entire new room onto his father Jacob's home by himself. This was his masterpiece created for his young bride. Any extra hours he could spare during the last months of his engagement had been given to the smallest details of their new home.

When his father and mother had revealed to him that they had secured the bride price for Mary he ran to the front door yelling, "Hallelujah," so loudly that the pet dog ran for his life. One did not usually fall in love with their bride before the wedding, but Joseph could not resist. She was beautiful, vibrant, intelligent, and known for her profound piousness. She was the woman every man in the village eyed as a wife, and now she would be Joseph's bride. He hugged his father and mother and let out another shout of delight. His parents smiled at their son's joy. Mary would make him complete.

The agreement had been negotiated almost six months ago. Very soon the engagement period would be over and Joseph would dress in his finest clothes and travel with a grand processional to the home of Mary's parents to receive his bride. Husband and wife would return to this very chamber and begin a new life together. They would become one flesh. He imagined a celebration that lasted a week. It would be the finest in the history of Nazareth. Who could have imagined that when his parents relocated here those many years ago that Joseph would find the woman of his dreams? "Who can understand the mind of Yahweh? His ways are surely above ours," thought Joseph with great comfort.

The year of engagement had been a time of preparation and patience and it was halfway through. Praise overtook Joseph like an escalating ocean swell causing him to dance in circles around the chamber. "Praise be to Yahweh for His goodness and great love. His timing is perfect. His sovereignty is beyond dispute. Could my life be any more blessed by Him?"

Christ, by highest heaven adored;
Christ, my everlasting Lord;
Late in time behold him come,
Offspring of the Virgin's womb.

Veiled in flesh the Godhead see;
Hail the incarnate Deity,
Pleased as man with men to dwell;
Jesus, our Emmanuel!

You are the Father whom I adore,
You are the Son forevermore;
You are the Spirit that has been sent.
Blessed Trinity, help me understand Your Advent.

Adapted from "Hark! The Herald Angels Sing" by Charles Wesley (1739)

There are many
   virtuous and capable
women in the world,
     but you
surpass them all!

Proverbs 31:29 (NLT)

Mary

What lies behind us and what lies before us
are tiny matters compared to what lies within us.
Oliver Wendell Holmes

Now in the sixth month [after that], the angel Gabriel was sent from
God to a town of Galilee named Nazareth, To a girl never having been
married and a virgin engaged to be married to a man whose name
was Joseph, a descendant of the house of David; and the virgin's name
was Mary. And he came to her and said, Hail, O favored one [endued
with grace]! The Lord is with you! Blessed (favored of God) are you
before all other women!
Luke 1:26–28 (AMP)

Mary sat on the floor of her home before the fire. She was preparing a special meal for her mother and father. These opportunities of blessing her much-loved parents would become rare in just a few months. Slowly grinding the meal for honey cakes, she stared into the bluish-orange flame and daydreamed about her wedding day. How big would the processional be? What would it sound like when it arrived? A bride never knew the hour that the bridegroom would come, so the entire day would be one of great anticipation. How would their guests be dressed? What gifts would they bring? She envisioned a great wedding feast that lasted days. There would be songs and dances of celebration that continued until the morning sun greeted the festive gathering. And what does the bridal chamber look like? Living in the close quarters of her family all her life, she tried to imagine a home of her own. All that space was a hard notion to wrap her mind around.

When her parents began to talk with Joseph's family about the possibility of marriage, Mary felt that it was a match they would not agree to. She was a young girl from a rather poor family, and he was a thriving carpenter who could have any woman in Nazareth that he desired. Yet for some reason he wanted her. They had known each other for a long time. They had laughed together and engaged in small talk on several occasions, but a simple look at each other in the market last year had changed everything. There was something in the way they stared at each other across the bustling bazaar that caused her to take notice of him in a very different way. It was not long afterward that Joseph's parents were inquiring of Mary's bride price. Mary's parents asked her what she thought about the match. "My prayers would be answered," was her blushing reply. Her love for Yahweh would be the only thing that ever outweighed her love for Joseph.

"What is Joseph doing right now?" she spoke out loud still staring into the glowing flame. "Is he thinking of me the way I am thinking of him?" Mary suddenly found herself mute as the feeling of electricity bolted through the air. The fire she was stirring started to engulf her surroundings, but she was not burning. She struggled to stand and had to hold herself against the wall to keep from falling over from the sense that the whole room was transforming into something different. Everything melted away as a figure of blinding brilliance began to materialize before her. Looking down, above, and around her, she saw nothing but stars. It was as if she had been transported into the midst of a crystal clear desert night where the sky stood bare before the earth like a waiting lover.

The figure was a sunburst exploding before her eyes, yet she could not look away. Mary felt as if she was suddenly transported to her wedding day but Yahweh, not Joseph, was her husband. The figure finally spoke although his mouth did not move. His voice sounded like a mountain breeze carrying the songs of a thousand priests:

Hail, O favored one! The Lord is with you! Blessed are you before all other women!

Come, Desire of nations come,
Fix in us Thy humble home;
Rise, the Woman's conquering Seed,
Bruise in us the Serpent's head.

Adam's likeness now efface:
Stamp Thine image in its place;
Second Adam, from above,
Reinstate us in thy love.

You are the Father whom I adore,
You are the Son forevermore;
You are the Spirit that has been sent.
Blessed Trinity, help me understand Your Advent.

Adapted from "Hark! The Herald Angels Sing" by Charles Wesley (1739)

You said,
"I have made a covenant with my
chosen one; I have sworn
to David my servant,
'I will establish
your line forever
and make your throne
firm through all generations'"

Psalm 89:3-4 (NIV)

Offspring
Everlasting

God moves in mysterious ways
His wonders to perform;
He plants His footsteps in the sea
And rides upon the storm.
William Cowper

But she was greatly troubled at the saying, and tried to discern what sort of greeting this might be. And the angel said to her, "Do not be afraid, Mary, for you have found favor with God. And behold, you will conceive in your womb and bear a son, and you shall call his name Jesus. He will be great and will be called the Son of the Most High. And the Lord God will give to him the throne of his father David, and he will reign over the house of Jacob forever, and of his kingdom there will be no end."

Luke 1:29–33 (ESV)

Mary was taken aback. But what Gabriel also noticed was that her first reaction to him was not the typical one. This girl, barely a woman, was unafraid of God's heavenly messenger. Throughout history, every human he had encountered assumed they were about to breathe their last breath when their eyes were opened to his presence. Until now. Mary's fear of Yahweh overshadowed her fear of all else, including this otherworldly being. It was what Gabriel said, not his imposing presence, that caused Mary to stagger. While he could tell she was wrestling with the meaning of his greeting, he was thinking to himself, "Who is this woman?"

Looking into her sable eyes that seemed ages beyond her years, Gabriel spoke a proclamation that would turn the darkness of the world on end. His words would put the Advent, the coming of Messiah, into motion. These were the words that all of heaven and earth longed for. They would spark life into a planet given over in the Terrible Rupture. The seed was about to spring up, the promise about to be fulfilled, and the kingdom of darkness would begin to fade. And it would all start with this tender Jewish peasant girl who sought God with her whole being and had dared to pray, "Lord, I will do anything you ask in my life. May Your will always be done through me." Who was this woman?

"Mary, you have nothing to be alarmed about. The God you greatly love has a gift beyond measure for you." Gabriel stopped to once again study her face. A peace poured over her like consecration oil on Aaron's beard. "Listen carefully favored one! You will become pregnant and give birth to a Son, and you shall name him Jeshua, Jehovah is Salvation." A small, crystalline tear began to form in the corner of her eye, yet she remained unfazed.

Gabriel continued with his announcement. "He will be great and will be called Son of the Most High; and the Lord God will give to Him the throne of his forefather David, and He will reign over the household of Jacob through the end of time and beyond, and there will be no earthly nor eternal boundary to His kingdom." With those words he saw wonder blossom in the girl's countenance. But it was not the words of the long-awaited coming of the Messiah, the Seed of David that confounded the young woman. Gabriel could see that Mary was perplexed that Yahweh would choose her to be the bearer of the Messiah.

Who was this woman?

She was the favored one and Gabriel began to tremble in her presence.

From heaven above to earth He comes,
To bear good news to every home,
Glad tidings of great joy He brings,
Of which now I will gladly sing.

Glory to God in highest heaven,
Who unto us His Son has given!
A little Child, of lowly birth,
Is now the joy of all the earth.

You are the Father whom I adore,
You are the Son forevermore;
You are the Spirit that has been sent.
Blessed Trinity, help me understand Your Advent.

Adapted from "From Heaven Above to Earth I Come" by Martin Luther (1531)

Therefore
the LORD himself
will give you a sign.
Behold, the virgin shall
conceive and bear a SON,
and shall call his name
Immanuel.

Isaiah 7:14 (ESV)

Virgin

I began to realize that I had believed countless things which I had never seen or which had taken place when I was not there to see, so many events in the history of the world, so many facts about places and towns which I had never seen, and so much that I believed on the word of friends or doctors or various other people.   Unless we took these things on trust, we should accomplish absolutely nothing in life.

St. Augustine, *Confessions* (Book VI, Chapter 5)

Mary said to the angel, "But how? I've never slept with a man." The angel answered, The Holy Spirit will come upon you, the power of the Highest hover over you; Therefore, the child you bring to birth will be called Holy, Son of God.

Luke 1:34–35 (THE MESSAGE)

Up to this point, Mary had assumed she was in a daydream. One minute she was cooking cakes and the next she stood before the Lord's herald as he spoke miraculous words; words that the chosen people had been waiting to hear throughout the years of the Great Silence. Messiah, the Son of God, was bringing a glorious salvation and His kingdom would be eternal. These revelations did not surprise the young woman from Nazareth. She never doubted God fulfilling His promise to save mankind.

What she did wonder was how she would be the vessel for the Messiah's introduction into the world. She was a virgin. In fact, she had never been alone with a man. She did not doubt that God would do something miraculous; she just wondered why God chose her. Looking directly into the sapphire-flame of the angel's eyes (was he trembling?), she asked a question with such purity and innocence that it struck the messenger mute for a few seconds. "How will God use me in this way since I have never been intimate with a man?" He stood in front of a woman of such faith that she dared ask to understand the greatest mystery the universe would ever see.

Communing with his Lord, the archangel asked for wisdom to answer the question that he himself could not grasp. A vision from the Master poured into his spirit. He was at the beginning of time, looking upon the Origin, the spark of creation, just after it had burst forward from the mouth of the Word. The heavens were alive with light and sound as stars burst into existence and planets aligned into a universal gravitational balance. The Milky Way was but a child. Gabriel was pulled past nebulas and constellations. Faster than the speed of light, he found himself on the third planet from a small sun within a solar system that did not seem any more special than any of the other billions of systems coming to life in the whole of creation.

Gabriel could see that this chosen world was formless and void of structure or any sort of ecosystem. It was a lifeless shell full of raw materials. Gabriel watched the unfathomable occur. The Holy Spirit of God appeared above the churning chaotic nothingness. Gabriel began to tremble in His presence. The Artist had arrived to create the canvas that would hold His masterpiece: His children. Gabriel carefully watched as that which was unexplainable to human or angelic intelligence happened in front of him. The Spirit deposited life into the formless void; the genesis spark that would multiply living beings into a dimension newly formed. For the first time, life would appear and produce more life. Gabriel was overwhelmed with the marvel of it all as he readied his answer to Mary.

Looking back into the girl's curious eyes, Gabriel spoke, "The Holy Spirit will come upon you, the power of the Highest will hover over you; therefore, the child you bring to birth will be called Holy, the Son of God." Somehow, those few words, coming from the heart of the Father, absorbed instantaneously into the heart of the young girl. She stood and simply received the revelation as truth.

Gabriel could only stare at her and reflect again, "Who is this woman?"

O come, all ye faithful,
Joyful and triumphant,
O come ye, O come ye to Bethlehem;
O Come, let us adore him, Christ the Lord.

God of God, Light of Light,
Lo! he despises not the Virgin's womb:
Very God, Begotten, not created;
O Come, let us adore him, Christ the Lord.

You are the Father whom I adore,
You are the Son forevermore;
You are the Spirit that has been sent.
Blessed Trinity, help me understand Your Advent.

Adapted from "O Come, All Ye Faithful" by John Francis Wade (1760)

But when the right time came,
God sent his Son who was
born of a woman and lived under
the law. God did this
so he could buy freedom
for those who were under the law
and so we could become
his children.

Galatians 4:4-5 (NCV)

Impossible

God is looking for people through whom He can do the impossible—what a pity that we plan only the things we can do ourselves.

A. W. Tozer

"And behold, your relative Elizabeth in her old age has also conceived a son, and this is the sixth month with her who was called barren. For nothing will be impossible with God." And Mary said, "Behold, I am the servant of the Lord; let it be to me according to your word." And the angel departed from her.

Luke 1:36–38 (ESV)

As he stood in front of the slight frame of the girl who would be the God-bearer, Gabriel had the look of one who was about to tell a secret he could barely contain. The archangel had looked forward to this particular moment since the day he spoke to Zachariah before the Holy of Holies. Mary noticed the odd expression on the angel's face, but trying to interpret it was like trying to read the emotions of a firestorm.

"Did you know that your cousin Elizabeth conceived a son, even in her twilight years? Even though the world thought her barren, she is now six months with child!" For the first time in their exchange, Mary had a look of genuine astonishment. "Nothing, you see, is impossible with God."

Mary looked deep into the flame, unafraid of incineration. Gabriel waited for what he now knew would be a fascinating response from this one, chosen from the foundation of creation as the womb of the Incarnation, the vessel that contained the Seed of the Advent. As she bowed her head in humble submission, Gabriel bent a knee in reverence. That simple act of humility ushered in the Presence of God in a way Gabriel had never experienced. Speaking in a whisper that reverberated throughout the universe and to the heavens beyond, Mary said, "Yes, I understand the will of the Father. I am his servant, devoted to His ways, His will, His heartbeat. He alone guides my steps and my life. Let it be with me according to all you have spoken and revealed."

Stillness fell again across the creation. A holy hush overtook and redeemed the Great Silence that had been in place for hundreds of years. And in this holy hush was a whisper of redemption for mankind. In the spark of Advent, the Holy Seed joined with a human egg and a Life unlike anything that the world would ever know was conceived within the womb of Mary.

Gabriel, the lone witness of God's divine romance, remained on his knees and wept tears that flowed like the mightiest falls on the blue orb. Mary watched as the powerful Gabriel slowly faded out of her vision.

Once again, Mary was alone on the floor of her home. Had she been absent seconds or hours? Reaching down, she put her hand on her belly. It was hot to the touch. She knew Life was within her womb. Looking down to the extinguished fire she saw that the cakes she had been baking for her parents were nothing but ash. They had become a burnt offering before the Lord.

Smiling, she whispered. "I am going to be a mother."

I see how the Virgin, drew near to gaze;
I too will thus bend my joyful knees;
I will embrace You, with love and awe;
Who would not love You, loving me so dearly?

Yes, Lord, I greet You,
Jesus, to Thee be glory given;
Word of the Father,
Now in flesh appearing;

You are the Father whom I adore,
You are the Son forevermore;
You are the Spirit that has been sent.
Blessed Trinity, help me understand Your Advent.

Adapted from "O Come, All Ye Faithful" by John Francis Wade (1760)

Blessed be God—
he heard me praying.
He proved he's on my side;
I've thrown my lot in with him.
Now I'm jumping for joy,
and shouting and singing
my thanks to him.

Psalm 28:6-7 (THE MESSAGE)

The Baby Leapt

*Blessed be God that Thou hast filled the soul of
Thy servant with joy and peace in believing.*
**Christopher Love, his prayer from the scaffold
immediately before his execution on August 22, 1651.**

*In those days Mary arose and went with haste into the hill country, to
a town in Judah, and she entered the house of Zechariah and greeted
Elizabeth. And when Elizabeth heard the greeting of Mary, the baby
leaped in her womb. And Elizabeth was filled with the Holy Spirit, and
she exclaimed with a loud cry, "Blessed are you among women, and
blessed is the fruit of your womb! And why is this granted to me that
the mother of my Lord should come to me? For behold, when the sound
of your greeting came to my ears, the baby in my womb leaped for joy.
And blessed is she who believed that there would be a fulfillment of
what was spoken to her from the Lord."*
Luke 1:39–45 (ESV)

The rest of Mary's week had been a flurry of unexpected activity. Her parents found her sitting in front of the fire on the floor of their home and thought she might be ill. "Mary?" Her mother touched her shoulder, "Are you well, my child?" Mary turned to her mother and father and said, "I am blessed beyond measure." A plan had come to Mary's mind over the last hour. She needed to tell her parents about her divine encounter, but under the proper circumstances. Standing up, Mary dusted the dirt and ash from her clothes. "Mary, where did all this soot come from?" asked Mary's father. "I burnt your honey cakes. I was thinking about cousin Elizabeth. We have been talking of visiting her and Zachariah for months. Let's visit them." Mary's mother thought about the upcoming wedding and how infrequent these moments would be in the near future. Turning to her husband who was still lamenting the burnt honey cakes, she spoke excitedly. "Husband, Mary is right. Let us take one final journey with our little girl before the wedding." "That sounds wonderful," replied Mary's father, now thinking about the coming absence of his only child. "But could you still make me some honey cakes? I love your honey cakes." "Yes father, I would be delighted to."

Mary sent word to Joseph about their unexpected trip to let him know she would return as soon as she was able. Within a day they had packed the mule and were on their way to the hill country of their roots. The journey was uneventful except for Mary's nonstop chatter. Her parents wondered why she was so excited. She seemed beyond herself as she talked about everything from the surprised look cousin Elizabeth would have upon their arrival to the coming of Messiah. Their only child kept them entertained. Her mother took note that Mary carried a sort of radiance she had not seen before. "Is this the look of an eager bride to be?" she wondered.

Three days later, the family entered the little village nestled between two hills. Stopping her parents, Mary said, "I am going to run ahead and surprise Elizabeth." She hugged them tightly, and kissed her mother on the cheek and her father on the forehead. Before they could say anything she was off with a leap and a dash toward the other side of the village. As her father watched her disappear behind a home he asked, "What has gotten into that girl?"

Elizabeth had only returned a few days before from her five months of seclusion. Her home was in desperate need of tidying and Zachariah was more than relieved to have her back. She was six months pregnant and the talk of the region. The last few days had been filled with a mixture of excited visitors and the catching up of household chores. When the door opened again she did not even turn around because of the abundance of visiting neighbors who wanted to see the fat miracle belly of an old lady with child.

"Surprise, Elizabeth! I have come to visit you and your baby." Elizabeth turned to see her beautiful young cousin who, unlike everyone else, seemed unfazed by her pregnancy. The baby in Elizabeth's womb, always active, felt as if he was leaping toward the young girl, so much so that Elizabeth lurched forward in the sensation. In a rush of invisible wind, Elizabeth was overflowing with God's Spirit. Throwing her hands in the air, she sang out in a voice that echoed off the heavens: "You're blessed among women, and the babe in your womb is also blessed! And why am I so blessed that the mother of my Lord visits me? The moment the sound of your greeting entered my ears, the babe in my womb skipped like a lamb for sheer joy. Blessed woman, who believed what God said, believed every word would come true!"

This visit would be anything but normal.

> My soul proclaims the greatness of the Lord,
> my spirit rejoices in God my Saviour;
> he has looked with favour on his lowly servant.
>
> From this day all generations will call me blessed;
> the Almighty has done great things for me and holy is his name.
>
> He has mercy on those who fear him,
> from generation to generation.

"Magnificat" (Part I), from the *Book of Common Worship*

Hannah prayed:
"The Lord has filled my heart
with joy; I feel very strong
in the Lord. I can laugh
at my enemies; I am glad because
you have helped me!"

"There is no one holy like the Lord.
There is no God but you;
there is no
Rock like our God."

1 Samuel 2:1-2 (NCV)

XVIII

Magnificat

Thoughts too deep to be expressed,
and too strong to be suppressed.
George Wither, from the poem "Her Beauty"

And Mary said, "My soul magnifies the Lord, and my spirit rejoices in God my Savior, for he has looked on the humble estate of his servant. For behold, from now on all generations will call me blessed; for he who is mighty has done great things for me, and holy is his name. And his mercy is for those who fear him from generation to generation. He has shown strength with his arm; he has scattered the proud in the thoughts of their hearts; he has brought down the mighty from their thrones and exalted those of humble estate; he has filled the hungry with good things, and the rich he has sent away empty. He has helped his servant Israel, in remembrance of his mercy, as he spoke to our fathers, to Abraham and to his offspring forever."
Luke 1:46–55 (ESV)

After Elizabeth's outburst of song, Mary started to laugh. The angel's fireside announcement was now her delight to behold. Mary loved to sing songs of old, especially psalms of praise to Yahweh. It seemed only appropriate to return Elizabeth's melodious greeting with a song that had been forming in her heart since the day of the angelic visitation. Closing her eyes and spinning around slowly she erupted in a song of adoration.

> "My soul magnifies and worships the Lord, and my spirit rejoices in God my Savior.
> He has seen me in my poverty, the humble place of His handmaiden.
> Behold! From this point forward every generation of every age will call me blessed. They will witness my abundant happiness and know that I was a chosen vessel. For He who is All-Powerful has done great things for me.
> His name is holy, His name is pure, and His name is majestic. Glory be to the Lord.
> His abundant mercy and kindness rests upon those who fear Him with a godly reverence, from generation to generation, throughout all ages.
> He has revealed His strength through His mighty arm; scattering those proud and puffed up in the imagination, direction and designs of their hearts.
> Pulling the powerful from their thrones and lifting up those of small stature, He fills and satisfies the hungry with good morsels, and He causes the rich to walk away empty handed.
> He has taken a hold of His servant Israel as a celebration of His mercy and love by fulfilling the same promises He lovingly gave to our ancestors, to Abraham and his descendants forever."

Mary spun herself to the ground, exhausted and exuberant in her laughter. Elizabeth's mouth was agape. Though she was stunned at Mary's sudden outburst of song and her lack of surprise at Elizabeth's pregnancy, it was the sudden revelation from God about this young woman carrying the Messiah in her womb that took Elizabeth aback. As she approached Mary, she did not know if she should warmly hug her or bow in honor of the Savior she carried.

"What are you doing on the ground you silly girl!" Mary's mother had come through the front door interrupting the scene. Elizabeth walked to her cousin, helped her off the ground, and gave her a hug. Mary's father saw

Elizabeth and let out a cry, grabbing his robe and ripping it in agony. "Cousin! Why did you not tell us of the tumor in your belly?" "Silly old man," said Elizabeth. "I am six months with child." As Mary's father turned red with embarrassment and tried to cover his exposed chest, her mother grabbed Elizabeth's hands and demanded the story of the miracle child. For the next few hours the family remained captivated as Elizabeth recalled the tale. Zachariah could only nod in agreement. "It is all so much to take in," said Mary's mother. "Mary, you have not blinked an eye at the story. What do you think?" "I think our God does miracles and loves us beyond our comprehension. Should this surprise any of us?" replied Mary. "What a very strange girl," said her father still trying to fix his ripped robe. As Mary spoke, Zachariah and Elizabeth saw a look of common experience in the young woman's eyes. The kind of look one has after meeting an archangel.

It was decided, under these new circumstances, that the family would stay and help throughout the rest of Elizabeth's pregnancy. Mary knew this was a part of God's providence. Her parents must be told about her divine pregnancy, but first she would share with her elder cousin. She was now with the one person, the only person in her world, who would understand her divine purpose. Walking to Elizabeth, Mary sunk against her pregnant belly and held her tightly. "It is good to be here."

He has shown strength with his arm
and has scattered the proud in their conceit,
Casting down the mighty from their thrones
and lifting up the lowly.

He has filled the hungry with good things
and sent the rich away empty.
He has come to the aid of his servant Israel,
to remember his promise of mercy,

The promise made to our ancestors,
to Abraham and his children forever.

"Magnificat" (Part II), from the *Book of Common Worship*

"He is a **voice** shouting in the wilderness, 'Prepare the way for the LORD's coming! Clear the road for him! The valleys will be **filled**, and the mountains and hills made level. The curves will be **straigtened**, and the rough places made smooth. And **then** all people will see the salvation sent from **God**.'"

Luke 3:4-6 (NLT)

John

XIX

Wonder is that feeling we get when we let go of our silly answers, our mapped out rules that we want God to follow. I don't think there is any better worship than wonder.

Donald Miller, *Blue Like Jazz*

When Elizabeth was full-term in her pregnancy, she bore a son. Her neighbors and relatives, seeing that God had overwhelmed her with mercy, celebrated with her. On the eighth day, they came to circumcise the child and were calling him Zachariah after his father. But his mother intervened: "No. He is to be called John." "But," they said, "no one in your family is named that." They used sign language to ask Zachariah what he wanted him named. Asking for a tablet, Zachariah wrote, "His name is to be John." That took everyone by surprise. Surprise followed surprise—Zachariah's mouth was now open, his tongue loose, and he was talking, praising God! A deep, reverential fear settled over the neighborhood, and in all that Judean hill country people talked about nothing else. Everyone who heard about it took it to heart, wondering, "What will become of this child? Clearly, God has his hand in this."

Luke 1:57–66 (THE MESSAGE)

As soon as she was alone with Elizabeth, Mary shared the miraculous tale of her angelic visitation. Trying to explain how she physically felt carrying the Seed of Abraham became impossible so she gave up and asked Elizabeth endless questions about her pregnancy. Telling her parents was difficult, but having Elizabeth at her side was the greatest of comforts. Her father and mother, by God's grace, hugged their little girl and cried tears of joy for her gift. Her utmost struggle came in pondering how she would tell Joseph and the embarrassment he would feel at the pregnancy. "Will he ever believe?" was her constant uncertainty.

The next three months was a time of great comfort for Mary. She loved being with her cousins and watching Elizabeth and Zachariah grow in excitement as the day of their child's birth grew closer. When the delivery day finally arrived, the midwife was quickly called. Rushing everyone out of the home except for Mary and her mother, the midwife created an atmosphere of peace and quiet so Elizabeth could concentrate on the task at hand. She would declare for years after that it was the smoothest birth she had ever assisted in. She would brag that Elizabeth had the constitution of a woman thirty years young and that she was as tough as a woman thirty years older. "I imagine the matriarch Sarah would have been proud of Elizabeth's labor." The next week would be filled with days of celebration as neighbors and relatives visited for a look at the miracle child.

On the eighth day, Jewish custom required the child's circumcision. The act of circumcision had been passed down thousands of years. Since the time of Abraham, it was the primary outward sign of God's covenant with His chosen people. It reminded them that they were not neglected and forgotten in the desert wasteland. Circumcision was the first act for the generation born in the wilderness before they stepped into the Promised Land. The cut represented more than just history, though, it portrayed God's desire for a people of pure heart—a people ready to hear, obey, and act on God's Word. It was also the day the child's name was first spoken aloud. That name, uttered at the cutting of flesh, would reveal the future of the child. The parents would choose a name that reflected the circumstances of the child's birth or feelings of gratitude toward God. Most considered it a prophecy of the child's future.

As soon as the baby was circumcised, the priest held the child up declaring him Zachariah. Poor Zachariah was mute so the priest assumed this was his desire. The crowd clapped at the child's name and for his future; that is until Elizabeth shouted "NO!" The jovial gathering came to an awkward hush. Elizabeth, now with the crowds undivided attention continued, "The child is to be called John," which means "Jehovah is a gracious giver." One of the village elders gave Elizabeth a stern look and decided to speak on the mute Zachariah's behalf. "Elizabeth, why would you name him that? No one in your family is named John." But she stood steadfast so the crowd turned to Zachariah and asked him what he wanted to name the child. Turning to a small child in the throng he asked for his clay tablet. The child, thrilled to be a part of the exchange, handed him the board. Scribbling his answer, Zachariah turned the board to the crowd which let out a collective gasp. It read: HIS NAME IS TO BE JOHN. Suddenly, Zachariah's tongue was liberated and he yelled aloud, "HIS NAME IS TO BE JOHN. PRAISE TO YOU LORD!" His sudden proclamation shook the unsuspecting crowd into a reverential fear. Zachariah's next words would remind Israel that the days of the Great Silence had come to an end.

Blessed be the Lord God of Israel:
for He has visited, and redeemed His people;
And has raised up a mighty salvation for us:
in the house of His servant David;

As He spoke by the mouth of His holy Prophets:
which have been since the world began;
That we should be saved from our enemies:
and from the hands of all that hate us;

To perform the mercy promised to our forefathers:
and to remember His holy covenant;
To perform the oath which He swore to our forefather Abraham:
that He would give us.

"Benedictus" (Part I), from the *Book of Common Prayer*

The Lord is my ROCK,
my Fortress, and my
Deliverer; my God, my keen
and firm Strength in Whom I will
trust and take refuge,
my Shield, and the Horn of
my salvation, my High Tower.

Psalm 18:2 (AMP)

The Benedictus

XX

I think that a life is not too long,
And therefore I determine,
That many people read a song,
Who will not read a sermon.
W. M. Praed, *Chant of the Brazen Head*

And his father Zechariah was filled with the Holy Spirit and prophe-
sied, saying, "Blessed be the Lord God of Israel, for he has visited and
redeemed his people and has raised up a horn of salvation for us in
the house of his servant David, as he spoke by the mouth of his holy
prophets from of old, that we should be saved from our enemies and
from the hand of all who hate us; to show the mercy promised to our
fathers and to remember his holy covenant, the oath that he swore to
our father Abraham, to grant us that we, being delivered from the
hand of our enemies, might serve him without fear, in holiness and
righteousness before him all our days. And you, child, will be called the
prophet of the Most High; for you will go before the Lord to prepare his
ways, to give knowledge of salvation to his people in the forgiveness of
their sins, because of the tender mercy of our God, whereby the sunrise
shall visit us from on high to give light to those who sit in darkness and
in the shadow of death, to guide our feet into the way of peace."
Luke 1:67–79 (ESV)

A Silent Wind filled Zachariah as the crowd stood in awe of his loosened tongue. Leaping in the air like a gazelle, he continued in thunderous praise, his deep voice reverberating beyond its natural state.

"Great blessing be to the Lord, the Sovereign of Israel, for He has visited His chosen people, bringing deliverance and redemption for all! The Author of salvation has raised a mighty horn to His lips that echoes from the house of His servant David." Many in the crowd fell to their knees while others began to weep, for God's Spirit permeated the entirety of the gathering.

"From the mouth of His holy prophets in ancient times the promise comes forth: WE WILL HAVE DELIVERANCE AND BE SAVED FROM OUR ENEMIES; FROM THE HANDS OF ALL WHO DETEST ISRAEL AND PURSUE THE DESTRUCTION OF GOD'S CHILDREN." Not a person in the crowd failed to think about their Roman overlords and the captivities that Israel experienced through their existence as a people.

Zachariah looked at young Mary, now three months with child. His voice softened as he began to sing God's love song to Mary as if she represented Israel. "He will show His abundant mercy, gracious compassion, and ceaseless kindness which He promised to our forefathers. His holy covenant will come to pass—the very same covenant He sealed with Abraham. Remember His covenant so that when He delivers us from our enemies, we will serve Him fearlessly, as a holy people, righteous within His Presence for all the days of our existence."

Walking to the priest that was holding his newborn son, he tenderly took the bundle of life into his arms. Looking upon the miracle child, tears began to fill the creases in his cheeks, formed by his aged smile. His song was now a whisper as he sang to the child. Those around him strained to hear, not wanting to miss a single word. "And you, little one, shall be called God's prophet; a prophet of the Most High. You shall walk before the face of the Lord to prepare His ways, His coming to earth. Bring and freely give the understanding of salvation to God's people for they will see complete forgiveness for their sins. They will walk in holiness."

Holding the child tightly, Zachariah's voice began to rise again as if he was addressing every corner of Israel, from the southern deserts to the northern mountains, from the Great Sea in the west to the gentile borders of the east. Little did he know his proclamation would travel throughout the entire globe.

"God's tender mercy and lovingkindness, the Aurora from on High, dawns upon us. He will visit us shining upon humanity by providing a guiding light to those sitting in the crushing darkness, chained to the shadow of death. He will grab our hopeless hands, liberate us, and lead us down the way of peace—never returning to captivity."

When Zachariah finally stopped his song of praise, he turned to Elizabeth and handed the child back to her. She was radiating with hope. Putting his arm around her, they walked through the frozen crowd back toward their home. Mary and her parents followed close behind. All other eyes were on the ground as prayers continued for the next few hours.

The story of the circumcision visitation would travel far and wide and the question on everyone's mind for years to come was, "Who will this child be for God's hand has been on this boy?"

> **That we being delivered out of the hands of our enemies:**
> **might serve Him without fear,**
> **In holiness and righteousness before Him:**
> **all the days of our life.**
>
> **And you, child, shall be called the Prophet of the Highest:**
> **for you shall go before the face of the Lord to prepare His ways;**
> **To give knowledge of salvation to His people:**
> **for the remission of their sins;**
>
> **Through the tender mercy of our God:**
> **whereby the day-spring from on high has visited us;**
> **To give light to them that sit in darkness, and in the shadow of death:**
> **and to guide our feet into the way of peace.**

"Benedictus" (Part II), from the *Book of Common Prayer*

Your life is a journey
you must travel
with a deep
consciousness
of God.

1 Peter 1:18 (THE MESSAGE)

Three Months

I am taking note that there are two ends to a voyage—what you go away from as well as what you go toward.
John Steinbeck, *The Acts of King Arthur and His Nobel Knights*

Mary stayed with Elizabeth for three months and then went back to her own home.
Luke 1:56 (THE MESSAGE)

Mary had not realized how much she missed the little village of Nazareth until she saw it on the hazy horizon. The journey home had been a colorless passage compared to the last three months with Elizabeth and Zachariah. Mary and her family departed a few days after the miraculous events of young John's circumcision. The parting from their cousins was filled with so many hugs that Mary thought she would pop like a bean if she was given just one more squeeze. Zachariah spent several hours of the last few days giving Mary elderly wisdom and words of encouragement. Although she would miss her cousins, Mary knew that it was time to go back to Nazareth. As Mary neared the city gates, her eagerness to return home was eclipsed by her apprehension for the next few months of her life.

It was true that she was filled with immeasurable joy and growing anticipation of the child that rested in her womb. But Mary's stomach clenched as she thought about the unavoidable meeting with her bridegroom. She had not been with Joseph since her miraculous pregnancy a little over a harvest season ago. She tried to convince herself that even though the reunion would be uncomfortable, it was a step in the glorious journey she was on. She needed to cling to Yahweh and His promises for her future care.

She thought back on the last few months. Her time with Elizabeth had been a perfect gift from Yahweh. Her swollen tummy would be obvious to all who saw her from now on. She knew mean rumors would spread like a locust plague. Rumors always worked their way through Nazareth with ease. She knew the gossip would be painful and she would likely be ostracized from her friends and relatives. This would bring tremendous embarrassment to Joseph. It was likely that he would demand a divorce. Lost in thought, Mary recalled a conversation she had with her cousin. "You must not expect him to understand. It would take the visitation of an angel for any human to comprehend what we know, dear one." Elizabeth always spoke in hushed tones when she talked of angels. "You will have to tell him the truth, but you must realize that he has to make a decision based only on what he sees," Elizabeth said as she pointed to Mary's growing belly. A consolation was that Mary's parents understood her gift from God. They would remain by her side.

When they reached their home in the village, Mary's mother began cleaning the house as if royalty was about to visit. She forbade Mary from doing a thing, knowing her heart was heavy with the thought of Joseph. Mary's father scuttled to the market to resupply the house with food for the next few days. Mary pondered in prayer for several hours before lighting a fire for the evening meal. The arrival of the family was the most exciting news of the day, and it did not take long before Joseph received word in his carpenter yard. Just hearing, "Mary's back!" was enough to get him to throw down his awl and hammer, untie his apron, and run across the village. Her name was like water to a man lost in the desert. Three months had seemed like thirty years.

He startled Mary as he entered the front door of her small home. Before she could rise from the fire on her own Joseph had picked her up and spun her around, yelling, "Oh, Mary! Never leave me again!" As Joseph put her down she felt his whole body stiffen with the embrace. Backing away, as if he had unknowingly hugged a viper, Joseph looked at Mary in disbelief. Before she could speak a word, he placed his hand on her stomach then pulled it away like it burnt him. Shaking his head in disbelief, he barely heard Mary say, "Joseph, we must talk . . ." as he sprinted out of her home.

Joseph did not hear her tears of anguish as he darted away from his awful dream.

Angels, from the realms of glory,
Wing your flight o'er all the earth;
Ye, who sang creation's story,
Now proclaim Messiah's birth:

Saints before the altar bending,
Watching long in hope and fear,
Suddenly the Lord descending,
In his temple shall appear:

You are the Father whom I adore,
You are the Son forevermore;
You are the Spirit that has been sent.
Blessed Trinity, help me understand Your Advent.

Adapted from "Angels, From the Realms of Glory"
by James Montgomery (1816)

If a man meets a virgin in a
city and has sexual relations
with her, but she is engaged to another
man, you must take both of them
to the city gate and put them to
death by throwing stones at them.
Kill the girl, because she was in a city
and did not scream for help.
And kill the man for having sexual
relations with another man's wife.
You must get rid of the evil
among you.

Deuteronomy 22:23-24 (NCV)

A Quiet Divorce

Nine months of awkward explanations, the lingering scent of scandal—it seems that God arranged the most humiliating circumstances possible for His existence, as if to avoid any chance of favoritism. I am impressed that when the Son of God became human . . . he played by the rules, harsh rules.

Phillip Yancey, *The Jesus I Never Knew*

This is how the birth of Jesus Christ came about. His mother Mary was engaged to marry Joseph, but before they married, she learned she was pregnant by the power of the Holy Spirit. Because Mary's husband, Joseph, was a good man, he did not want to disgrace her in public, so he planned to divorce her secretly.

Matthew 1:18–19 (NCV)

He ran and kept running until he collapsed from exhaustion a few miles outside of Nazareth. He had come to a rocky place, taking solace under the shade of a lone tree. "Why Lord? Why has she been unfaithful?" Joseph felt as though the agony was putting chains around his heart and pulling him to the center of Hades. Mary was known for her unusual piety and godly kindness. How could she, more than any other woman, have turned her back on their promised covenant? Confusion was chipping away at Joseph like an awl to the plank, and the chips seemed to be piling up around him. Their wedding was only three months away. Every day Joseph visited the bridal chamber he had created for Mary. He would sit in one of the handcrafted chairs and pray for his bride and their future together. Many times he found himself singing praises to Yahweh for the blessing Mary would be in his life. That room, once a sanctuary for Joseph, now seemed like a tomb that would imprison his dream of the future.

What would the townspeople say when they found out about Mary's unfaithfulness? Maybe they would assume it was Joseph who impregnated the girl because he could not wait for their wedding night. How would he prove it was not true? How could he demonstrate his righteousness? It was Mary who sinned against Yahweh and Joseph. The Law made provision for a case such as this. "Yes. I could make her an example for the pain she has caused me." His volatile anger was turning the normally levelheaded man into something dangerous. "She deserves public disgrace." If she would not admit her sin, Joseph could invoke the right of a stoning. She was an engaged woman who had been unfaithful. Breaking her marriage covenant was not something to be dealt with lightly. It was his right to march back into Nazareth and drag her before the city gates, exposing her iniquity. He would demand the men stone her for her trespass.

As he picked up a jagged stone he thought about the Law, his rights, and Mary's death. Looking down, he noticed blood was dripping out of his fist. He was squeezing the stone so tightly that he had cut himself. He dropped the toothed rock and looked at his bloodied palm and fingers. "What am I thinking?" Falling to the ground, Joseph began to weep, not at how he had been wronged nor at what he had lost, but at how easy he was becoming something he detested. Anger was driving him like a bitter scourge. The blood continued to flow from the cuts on his hand, but seeing his own blood only made him think of the ground that would be covered by Mary's blood. And what about the baby in her womb? What had that child done to him?

Joseph knew that regardless of Mary's impropriety, he loved her. Marriage would be out of the question. He would not be able to get past her unfaithfulness, but he wanted no harm to come to the girl or the baby she carried. There would be no stoning or public exposure from Joseph.

Sitting amongst the scattered stones, he began to think about the action he must take. He would not bring Mary shame nor open disgrace. She would bring that upon herself over the next few months as others noticed her pregnancy. Instead, he would quietly and discreetly write up a divorce dismissal and attempt to put his life back in order. It was the most he could do for the woman he loved; a woman who had broken his spirit. Picking himself up off the ground, he started the slow, painful walk back to Nazareth, now a city of sorrow for him.

With the woes of sin and strife
The world has suffered long;
Beneath the angel-strain have rolled
Two thousand years of wrong;

"Peace on the earth, goodwill to men,
From heaven's all-gracious King."
The world in solemn stillness lay,
To hear the angels sing.

You are the Father whom I adore,
You are the Son forevermore;
You are the Spirit that has been sent.
Blessed Trinity, help me understand Your Advent.

Adapted from "It Came Upon a Midnight Clear" by Edmund Sears (1849)

"No longer will a man teach his neighbor, or a man his brother, saying, 'Know the LORD,' because they will all know me, from the least of them to the greatest," declares the LORD. "For I will forgive their wickedness and will remember their sins no more."

Jeremiah 31:34 (NIV)

Dream

We are such stuff as dreams are made on;
and our little life is rounded with a sleep.
Shakespeare, *The Tempest*

While he was trying to figure a way out, he had a dream. God's angel spoke in the dream: "Joseph, son of David, don't hesitate to get married. Mary's pregnancy is Spirit-conceived. God's Holy Spirit has made her pregnant. She will bring a son to birth, and when she does, you, Joseph, will name him Jesus—'God saves'—because he will save his people from their sins."
Matthew 1:20–21 (THE MESSAGE)

Upon entering his home, Joseph's father, Jacob, looked at his son's face. "Have you been crying?" Joseph's reply was slow and somber. "It is nothing father. I have a lot on my mind. I need some time to think and be alone for a bit." "Your hand! You have cut it. Let me look at it." Joseph's hand was wrapped in a bit of cloth he had ripped off his cloak. The bleeding had finally stopped on his walk back to Nazareth, but the grey strip of fabric was soaked crimson. Walking to his father, he grabbed him and held him tightly. It took everything he had to hold back from sobbing in his father's embrace. He felt like a little boy looking to his dad for comfort after an accident. "I am fine, father, but I need some time to myself. Can you give me that for a few minutes?" "Of course, son. I am here when you are ready to talk," Jacob answered in a worried tone.

It was painful to enter the bedchamber that he had built over the last nine months, but it was a quiet place where he would not be disturbed. Walking over to the wedding chest he had crafted for Mary, he deliberately ran his fingers over the Hebrew lettering he had engraved into it. Tracing the carved words with his fingers did not bring comfort. TRUST IN YHWH WITH ALL YOUR HEART AND DO NOT LEAN ON YOUR OWN UNDERSTANDING. The passage from the Proverbs had been his guiding light for as long as he could speak Hebrew. "How do I trust now, Lord? What do I do?" Silence was his only answer. As he lay on the bed that he had built for his wedding night, he smelled the fresh hay, still curing for a coupling that would never happen. Planting his face in the mattress, he began to weep and pray. Somewhere in the mixture of salty tears Joseph's exhausted body, racked with sorrow and confusion, gave itself over to an undisturbed sleep.

Joseph awoke sitting in the stony field again. The sky, the rocks, even his body was stained a dingy brown color. But now he was imprisoned by countless blade-sharp stones that trapped him in all directions. Suddenly, a rip in the air appeared just a few feet in front of him. A world of color was breaking through his monochrome world. A being of perilous beauty and power stepped through the rip as if it was a curtain. He was glorious to behold, and a rainbow of colors was jetting forth from his presence. You could look through him like you were looking through a thin sheet of fabric. The world beyond him was in full color. His face was kind and fierce all in the same moment, causing Joseph to be both terrified and comforted.

The Rainbow-Being began to speak to the dumbfounded man on the ground. "Joseph, son of David, do not be afraid." Joseph noticed that the Being's words flowed out of his mouth in the bright hues of a million different flowers. "Take Mary as your bride, for the child who is in her womb is conceived of the Holy Spirit." The brightness of those words caused Joseph to cover his eyes. In that moment everything became clear. "The Favored One will bear a Son, and you shall name Him Jesus, for He will save His people from their sins and restore them to God's presence." Before Joseph could open his eyes, the Being was gone and Joseph was sitting in a field full of an infinite number of flowers each distinctive in color, type, and aroma. Joseph began to breathe in the perfumed air, but all he could smell was fresh cut hay.

He awoke in the bed and suddenly sat up. His grief had been replaced with uncontainable joy. "Mary! I must see Mary!" were the words he yelled to his father as he ran out of the door.

> And man, at war with man, hears not
> The love-song which they bring;
> And I, beneath life's crushing load,
> Whose form is bending low.
>
> "Peace on the earth, goodwill to men,
> From heaven's all-gracious King."
> Do I in solemn stillness lay,
> To hear the angels sing.
>
> You are the Father whom I adore,
> You are the Son forevermore;
> You are the Spirit that has been sent.
> Blessed Trinity, help me understand Your Advent.

Adapted from "It Came Upon a Midnight Clear" by Edmund Sears (1849)

Being asked by the Pharisees
when the kingdom of God would come,
he answered them, "The kingdom
of God is not coming with signs
to be observed, nor will they say,
'Look, here it is!' or
'There!' for behold,
the kingdom of God
is in the midst of you."

Luke 17:20–21 (ESV)

God with Us

The world everywhere gives evidence of a vanished God and man in all his actions gives evidence of a longing for that God.

Blaise Pascal

This would bring the prophet's embryonic sermon to full term: Watch for this—a virgin will get pregnant and bear a son; They will name him Immanuel (Hebrew for "God is with us").

Matthew 1:22–23 (THE MESSAGE)

Lucis watched from the Otherworld as Joseph ran from his home to the woman that fulfilled his deepest desires. Finally, Joseph knew she carried the child that would heal this lost world's wounds. Lucis wanted to soar throughout the universe and proclaim the coming of the Messiah. No human or angel had grasped the journey that the Trinity had planned before the creation of the world. He longed to enter the gates of paradise and pronounce the Creator's greatest mystery as revealed.

But Lucis's purpose was not proclaiming the story that was unfolding before his angelic eyes, but rather chronicling it. Finding a quiet place on a budding planet, Lucis collected his thoughts. Pulling out his writing materials, he began to scroll through all that had occurred. The story of Elizabeth and Zachariah had some odd twists and turns. The profound steps the Lord took to prepare for the Son's forerunner, John, brought ecstasy to Lucis's pen. But that story was nothing but foreshadow to what Lucis knew was the greatest love story in the short history of mankind. Though Joseph and Mary had been orchestrated into a relationship that would span the ages, it was not their story that Lucis considered the greatest. It was God's pursuant passion for a people who seemed to forever scorn His love for them.

He thought back to the prophet Hosea whose own story was one of Israel's greatest tales of tragedy and triumph. The woman Hosea married, the mother of his children, would turn her back on the prophet to pursue the affections and beds of other men. In time, the woman Gomer would leave her home and partake in the life of a prostitute until there was nothing left of her. The very men who drained her of life left her to die outside of Hosea's home. And how did Hosea repay Gomer's scorn? He brought her back in and spent months restoring her to health. Eventually, she became, once again, his beautiful bride, but this time she loved him more than any other woman loved any other man in the history of Israel. She would love him not for what he could do for her but for the mercy and steadfast love that he showed for her when she hated him.

The God of Israel was returning for his chosen people, but not as a triumphant Otherworldly warrior. He did not come to bring judgment to a scornful people or terror to those who worshiped false gods. He was not coming loaded with material riches for His faithful followers or to prove His existence to an unbelieving world. He came as a human child. Yahweh, Creator of All, Alpha and Omega was going to wrap Himself in the flesh of a newborn Israelite babe. Omnipotence would place Himself in helplessness, needing a mother to feed Him by the breast and a father to provide protection. Omniscience would be a young boy who would have to learn how to walk and talk. Trinity would become Man. That Man would be subject to weather, hunger, sadness, pain, and the effects of sin on this broken world. He would play by human rules. Yet, He would remain Trinity.

Lucis still did not understand the plans of the Almighty but he did not doubt His wisdom and His endless love. Yahweh would be near! As near as any human on the blue orb could imagine. Even now He nestled in the womb of a young Israelite girl. As he started his journey back to earth, Lucis shouted as if the entire universe could hear his proclamation, "God will come in the flesh, incarnate, and touchable! There will never be a tale that men will want to find truer than this!"

> Oh holy night! The stars are brightly shining
> Long lay the world in sin and error pining
> Till he appear'd and the soul felt its worth.
> A thrill of hope the weary world rejoices
>
> I fall on my knees to hear the angel voices
> Oh night divine, Oh night when Christ was born
> Oh night divine, Oh night divine
> For yonder breaks a new and glorious morn!
>
> You are the Father whom I adore,
> You are the Son forevermore;
> You are the Spirit that has been sent.
> Blessed Trinity, help me understand Your Advent.

Adapted from "O Holy Night" by Adolphe Adam (1847)

But now, O Jehovah,
thou art our Father;
we are the clay,
and thou our potter;
and we all are the work
of thy hand.

Isaiah 64:8 (ASV)

A Secret Wedding

Sometimes I imagine that I am a piece of stone, waiting for the sculptor. When I give myself to God this way, He begins sculpting my soul into the perfect image of His beloved Son.

Brother Lawrence, *The Practice of the Presence of God*

And Joseph awoke from his sleep and did as the angel of the Lord commanded him, and took Mary as his wife, but kept her a virgin until she gave birth to a Son.

Matthew 1:24–25a (NASB)

Joseph wove in and out of the homes and marketplace with the speed of a desert hare to get to Mary's home. Many stopped as he ran by wondering what the trouble was until they heard the hearty laughter that followed him like an invisible trail marker. As he came around a corner, Joseph barely missed knocking over one of the fussy local women coming home from the market. "Will that carpenter ever grow up? For heaven's sake he is about to be a married man!" The thought of scandal and a ruined reputation had long departed Joseph's mind.

As Mary's home came into view, Joseph intentionally slowed his pace. He did not want to make a scene in front of the neighbors who were starting to congregate around their homes in the coolness of the oncoming evening. Coming to her front door he looked in. "Excuse me. May I enter?" he humbly asked to Mary's mother and father who were standing guard over their daughter. "That would not be such a good idea," said Mary's father in a protective tone. "Please, Mary. It is important." The way he had stormed out yesterday gave Mary pause, but she allowed him to join the family. Her mother and father's feet were planted as roots. They would hear anything he had to say to their daughter.

"Mary, I have been a fool." His words were deliberate and carefully chosen. "I assumed when you returned from your cousins that you had been unfaithful to me. I was so excited to see you after your long absence that the shock of feeling your swollen belly . . . it was too much. Please forgive me for my reaction. I was foolish and thoughtless." Mary looked down and spoke softly. "You were forgiven before you ever left. I knew this might not go well. I wanted to tell you, but I knew you would not believe. . . . What happened to your hand?" Joseph walked over and hugged Mary, silencing her in the middle of her explanation. "You don't have to prove anything, my love. I know what has happened. I have been visited by an angel in a dream. I know that you carry Messiah! You will be the mother of the Son of God." Mary began to softly weep for the wonder of it all. "I only have one question for you. Will you allow this foolish lump of clay to be your husband? I promise, I will allow Yahweh to mold me into the vessel that helps you raise the Gift-child in your womb." "Yes, Joseph! Yes! There is nothing more that would please my heart." And with that they embraced and held each other tightly knowing the Divine Seed was now their inspiration for marriage. Mary's mother began to cry. She turned to her husband, who was dumbfounded at what just occurred in front of him, and said, "I love you, you silly old man."

Joseph decided they must make haste so a secret wedding would be in order. After going home he explained his dream to his parents. They were stunned at the happenings of Yahweh that had taken place the last few months. Joseph then prepared the wedding chamber. It was the following evening when his beautiful young bride arrived at his parent's home. A slightly confused priest performed an evening wedding unlike any he had done before. Even though it violated custom, he agreed to perform the ceremony. Joseph and Mary looked like any young couple about to be married. It was simple and beautiful. There would be no formal celebration. The newly married couple would enter their wedding chamber, and their parents would dine together for a most interesting evening of conversation.

As Joseph lit the lamps to illuminate the wedding chamber, Mary was overcome with emotion as she saw the care and love put into every detail of her new home. Joseph invited her to the new bed. Mary smelled the fresh cut straw. Lying down next to Joseph, the Virgin-Mother felt safe. She snuggled close to him, falling asleep in his arms. As Joseph began to slumber he thought he caught the scent, for just a moment, of a thousand flowers.

Oh holy night! The stars are brightly shining.
Truly He taught us to love one another.
His law is love and His gospel is peace,
for yonder breaks a new and glorious morn!

Chains shall He break for the slave who is our brother,
and in His name all oppression shall cease.
Sweet hymns of joy in grateful chorus raise we,
let all within us praise His holy name.

You are the Father whom I adore,
You are the Son forevermore;
You are the Spirit that has been sent.
Blessed Trinity, help me understand Your Advent.

Adapted from "O Holy Night" by Adolphe Adam (1847)

Bethlehem Ephrath, you are one of the smallest towns in the nation of Judah. But the LORD will choose one of your people to rule the nation—someone whose family goes back to ancient times.

Micah 5:2 (CEV)

Bethlehem

To determine to go and to say it
was to be halfway there.
John Steinbeck, *The Pearl*

About that time Caesar Augustus ordered a census to be taken
throughout the Empire. This was the first census when Quirinius was
governor of Syria. Everyone had to travel to his own ancestral home-
town to be accounted for. So Joseph went from the Galilean town of
Nazareth up to Bethlehem in Judah, David's town, for the census. As
a descendant of David, he had to go there. He went with Mary, his
fiancée, who was pregnant.
Luke 2:1–5 (THE MESSAGE)

Over the next five months, Joseph and Mary enjoyed life as newlyweds but without the consummation of their marriage covenant. But that did not matter. They were in love and their calling as the soon-to-be parents of the Messiah was a covenant stronger than any on earth. Mary lived in the new home and began to settle nicely into her fresh pace of life.

The rumors came as expected. Whispers in the marketplace as the young couple passed by only increased as Mary's body began to adapt to oncoming motherhood. But the gossipers were confused. They knew something happened to Mary while away with her cousins, but Joseph acted as if her impropriety did not matter in the least to him. In fact, if the ladies of Nazareth did not know better, it appeared that Joseph was ecstatic about Mary's pregnancy. And his joy became infectious, eventually silencing all the naysayers.

Just as the newlywed couple assumed their future was set on solid ground, their world was once again shaken. About a month before Mary's due date, Caesar Augustus, supreme ruler of the Roman Empire, declared it was time to pad the realm's coffers, now greatly in need of money for future projects throughout the world. To collect the necessary taxes, all the citizens of the Roman Empire were required to register for a census in their ancestral homes. All lives, wherever they were and whatever they did, were rerouted until the head of each family presented the proper documents to the Roman authorities. Resisting the census could amount to financial ruin or imprisonment. For Joseph, this meant returning to the little community of Bethlehem. During most of Joseph's life, a voyage to Bethlehem fueled his imagination. Not only would he attend the most entertaining family reunions where rich delicacies and plentiful frolicking were daily happenings, but he would visit the birthplace of Israel's greatest king, David. As a child he walked through the very fields where the musician David wrote some of the psalms while protecting his family's flocks. Bethlehem was known as the House of Bread, and for Joseph it was a place of spiritual sustenance.

But this journey would be anything but exciting. Joseph and Mary discussed two options. Mary could stay in Nazareth with her family. It was safe, smart, and logical. But neither of them was comfortable with the safe decision. Mary knew she was close to the birth of her child and she wanted Joseph, more than anyone else, by her side. The journey would be relatively secure because there would be large crowds moving to their ancestral homes all over Israel in the next few weeks. But riding for days on the back of a donkey, with minimal supplies and under the scrutiny of the weather, in her current physical condition would be a challenge for Mary. As much as both of their families tried to talk them out of it, Joseph and Mary were set on making this journey together. Yahweh had started this strange course of events and He would see them through.

They packed up their donkey for the trip south, then Joseph prayed while their families surrounded them in support. Mary's father invoked a word from the prophet Micah that brought a great deal of comfort to the small gathering, "I heard this prophecy from the scroll of Micah a few days ago. May we all take comfort in the words of the prophet: 'Bethlehem Ephrath, you are one of the smallest towns in the nation of Judah. But Yahweh will choose one of your people to rule the nation—someone whose family goes back to ancient times.'" With that, the families hugged their children and watched them as they rode out of the gate of Nazareth into the arms of God.

O little town of Bethlehem, How still we see you lie!
Above your deep and dreamless sleep the silent stars go by;
Yet in your dark streets shines the everlasting Light;
The hopes and fears of all the years are met in you tonight.

For Christ is born of Mary, and gathered all above,
While mortals sleep, the angels keep their watch of wondering love.
O morning stars, together proclaim the holy birth!
And praises sing to God the King, and peace to men on earth.

You are the Father whom I adore,
You are the Son forevermore;
You are the Spirit that has been sent.
Blessed Trinity, help me understand Your Advent.

Adapted from "O Little Town of Bethlehem" by Phillips Brookes (1868)

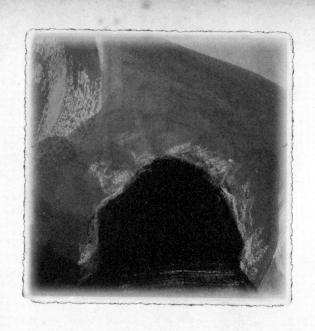

In love a throne will be
established; in faithfulness a
man will sit on it—one from
the house of David—one who in
judging seeks justice
and speeds the cause of
righteousness.

Isaiah 16:5 (NIV)

No Room

We have to embrace the Bible as the wild, uncensored, passionate account it is of people experiencing the living God. Doubting the one true God. Wrestling with, arguing with, reconciling with, loving, worshipping, thanking, following the one who gives us everything. We cannot tame it. We cannot tone it down. If we do, then we can't say it is the life-giving Word of God. We have made it something else.

Rob Bell, *Velvet Elvis*

And while they were there, the time came for her delivery . . . there was no room or place for them in the inn.
Luke 2:6, 7b (AMP)

The last few hours, Joseph had felt like a fish swimming against the current, but the current was a tide of bodies. The couple had arrived on the outskirts of Jerusalem after an easier than expected journey from Nazareth. The roads had been busy, causing the time to pass quickly with the many conversations they engaged in on their way to Bethlehem. The weather had been lovely, and Mary was so aflutter with the approaching Child that she barely felt any discomfort. As they started to skirt around Jerusalem on their way south, they noticed the masses of people camping outside the city. Joseph had not taken into account how many citizens' roots were in the City of David. It was not even this crowded during the great Jewish celebrations.

Bethlehem sat a few miles south of Jerusalem. During the easy afternoon journey the crowds never abated. That is when the labor pains began. Even though she could feel contractions beginning, Mary experienced a sense of excitement as if an unhindered sun was about to crest the horizon after years of darkness. She prayed her water would not break on the bumpy donkey ride. Joseph knew they had to get to Bethlehem quickly, but his hope for finding a place to lodge for the night was growing thinner every mile. Because of the erratic governor, Herod, Joseph's family had fled Bethlehem years ago so his only hope was to find an inn for them to spend the evening. For the birth of a child, private clean quarters would be necessary. Joseph found himself praying desperate, silent prayers as not to alert Mary. "Lord, you have led us every step of the way. He is your Son. I know you will provide what we need."

But Bethlehem was a madhouse of activity. Mary sat quietly on the donkey listening to Joseph's requests to locals a hundred times over. "Please sir, my wife is about to give birth. We need a place to stay tonight. Do you have a room available?" A hundred different answers came back to the couple. "Can't you see how busy everything is?" "You will have no luck in this place this week." "It's the government stealing from its citizens!" "You are one of a thousand victims." "I wish I could help you." "May God bless you and your wife. Now move on." It did not matter how many times Joseph heard the excuses. Every apology drained the life out of him until he found himself praying out loud, no longer able to contain his frustration. "Lord, do You not care about Your own Son? Do You want Him born in the dirt? Where are You?"

Mary let Joseph rain down his pent up emotions. She carefully moved off the donkey and walked over to him, putting her arms around his slumped neck. "Joseph, we are His children. He will have what He wills." They were close to the center of

Bethlehem and they had climbed to one of the highest points around. Looking out over the shepherds' fields that surrounded the town and seeing the bright evening lights of Jerusalem in the distance brought a peace to Joseph. Yahweh was their Light and their Shepherd. Both prayed silent prayers. "Your will be done."

"You! Young man, why are you sitting in the middle of the street with a woman ready to burst with child?" An old woman was yelling out of the window of the last inn they visited. They were told it was quite full. Joseph yelled up to the woman explaining their plight and Mary's condition. Within minutes, the old woman had scampered down. "There is no space, true enough. My husband and I run this establishment. I cannot offer you a room, nor can anyone for miles around, but I do have another alternative if you are not too proud to accept it." "We are thankful for whatever shelter we can find," said Mary. Smiling, the old woman said, "Then follow me."

Below the inn lay a cave dug into the limestone bedrock. It was dry and full of donkeys and sheep. It was used for travelers with livestock. There was a small niche in the front of the cave for a caretaker-shepherd. A small fire was already blazing. Removing the caretaker for the night, the woman offered the humble shelter to the couple. Joseph surveyed his surroundings and grabbed the old woman in an embrace. "It is perfect. We will take it."

O holy Child of Bethlehem!
Descend to me, I pray;
Cast out my sin and enter in,
Be born in me today.

I hear the Christmas angels
The great glad tidings tell;
O come to me, abide with me,
My Lord Emmanuel!

You are the Father whom I adore,
You are the Son forevermore;
You are the Spirit that has been sent.
Blessed Trinity, help me understand Your Advent.

Adapted from "O Little Town of Bethlehem" by Phillips Brookes (1868)

Simon Peter
arrived and went into
the tomb and saw
the strips of linen
lying there.

John 20:6 (NCV)

Clothed

There are people who are clad in tunics and who have nothing to do with furs who, nevertheless, are lacking in humility. Surely humility in furs is better then pride in tunics.

St. Bernard of Clairvaux

The time came for her delivery, And she gave birth to her Son, her Firstborn; and she wrapped Him in swaddling clothes and laid Him in a manger.

Luke 2:6b–7a (AMP)

Joseph wasted no time in preparing the makeshift shelter into the birth place for the coming Messiah. The old woman brought water from the well and had the caretaker-shepherd bring cut hay for the young girl to lie on. Joseph used some of the water to ease Mary's travel thirst. He boiled the rest in preparation for the newborn. Then both shepherd and innkeeper left for the evening to tend to the over-packed hostel above. Cleaning the cave in an attempt to make a comfortable surrounding for Mary, Joseph found his vigor fueled by the Advent of the Messiah.

"How are you feeling?" he asked Mary. "It is not as I imagined," she said. "I know, my love," Joseph comforted, "I did not expect you to give birth in a barn." "No, that is not what I mean. I thought I would be more nervous, but I am happy," she said. Joseph was silenced. She continued, "We are surrounded by livestock, squatters in the City of Bread. We have no family around. No midwife tends my side. I am tired and sore. Yet, I have never felt more peace in my entire life. We are to be parents!" Joseph walked over to Mary and placed his hands upon her cheek. Looking into her sable eyes he kissed her on the forehead and said, "Who is this woman who bares the Son of God?"

When the time of birth came, Mary remained focused, talking Joseph through midwife duties he never imagined he would ever be a part of. Men rarely saw the birth of their children. Joseph found it exhilarating. As Mary squatted, holding onto natural limestone handholds in the wall, Joseph waited beneath for the child to emerge. The labor ended in minutes. Mary pushed with all her strength, but there was no pain. The Child came quickly as if He could not wait to come into the world of men. Joseph cut the cord and Mary lowered herself to the fresh hay covered over by a clean blanket Joseph brought from home.

She fixed her eyes on Joseph who started to clean the helpless Child. The Baby cooed and made quiet noises, but never screamed. As Joseph rubbed salt on the Baby, to help dry and firm the skin, he thought the Child was studying him. He knew this was impossible. Seeing the naked Infant stirred him more than his angelic dream encounter. He wanted to weep for joy in the presence of the Babe, but he had another job to do. He handed the Baby back to Mary along with the swaddling bands of cloth that they had carried in their pack from Nazareth. Mary took the long narrow strips of fresh cloth and began wrapping the Baby like a little mummy. Usually, the mother of a newborn wrapped the child to protect their weak limbs and hold in body heat. This would be important on this chilly evening. She wrapped Him as if each bandage was a part of her heart. She wrapped till He was wrapped in both cloth and her love. In that moment she did not think about how this Child was Yahweh wrapped in humanity. Right now He was just her newborn son.

Joseph stayed busy creating a crib. He found a small clay trough that the sheep were feeding from. Emptying its contents, he wiped it as clean as he could. He washed and dried it then filled it with the fresh hay. Then Joseph placed a blanket down and then another. Bringing the manger over to Mary he said, "Look, our little King has a crib fit for royalty." Both laughed at the irony and pure joy of the moment.

Placing the child in the manger, both parents froze in thought. They did not say what they both saw: "It looks like we are placing a tiny body into a grave." This minute was too sweet for such morbid observations. Mary broke the silence, "welcome little One, to the world You will save."

Away in a manger, no crib for a bed,
The little Lord Jesus laid down his sweet head.
The stars in the bright sky looked down where he lay,
The little Lord Jesus asleep on the hay.

I love thee, Lord Jesus! Look down from the sky,
And stay by my side 'til morning is nigh.
Be near me Lord Jesus, I ask you to stay.
Close by me forever, And love me I pray.

You are the Father whom I adore,
You are the Son forevermore;
You are the Spirit that has been sent.
Blessed Trinity, help me understand Your Advent.

Adapted from "Away in a Manger" (1885)

He named
the baby
Jesus.

Matthew 1:25 (The Message)

Jesus

There was a man born among these Jews who claimed to be, or to be the son of, or to be "one with," the Something which is at once the awful haunter of nature and the giver of moral law. This claim is so shocking—a paradox, and even a horror, which may easily be lulled into taking too lightly—that only two views of this man are possible. Either he was a raving lunatic of an unusually abominable type, or else He was, and is, precisely what He said. There is no middle way.

C. S. Lewis, *The Problem of Pain*

God's angel spoke in the dream: "Joseph, son of David, don't hesitate to get married. Mary's pregnancy is Spirit-conceived. God's Holy Spirit has made her pregnant. She will bring a son to birth, and when she does, you, Joseph, will name him Jesus—'God saves'—because he will save his people from their sins."

Matthew 1:20–21 (THE MESSAGE)

Joseph sat next to Mary on a fresh blanket he laid upon the hay. The new parents stared at the Babe that now lay in the makeshift crib. They had often discussed what this experience would be like, but nothing captured the wonder. According to tradition, the Child would be named publically by his father during the circumcision ceremony. But nothing, absolutely nothing that surrounded the circumstances of this Child's birth followed any traditional patterns. The covenant, once communicated through the Word of God, would now show itself in the life of a Human. The Advent was now visible in human flesh.

Mother and father heard the Child begin to stir with hunger. Gently lifting the Babe, Joseph handed Him to Mary who put Him to her breast bringing nourishment to the Human-Divine. Looking down upon the suckling Child, Joseph whispered the Name that would cause the universe to leap in ecstatic bliss. "Little One. You will be known as Jesus." Mary responded with a tearful whisper, "Jesus."

The invisible realm, upon hearing the Name above all names, would have a different reaction. Mary and Joseph were unaware of the hundreds of thousands of angelic beings that had gathered from every corner of the invisible realm to surround the little hillside cave in Bethlehem. They had watched the divine birth in absolute silence. Never had the whole angelic species gathered in one place at the same time. At the whisper of "Jesus" they were all compelled to fall on their faces in heavenly worship. Their spirits were opened to a miracle beyond their otherworldly comprehension. Where Mary and Joseph saw a cradle, the angelic realm saw a throne. Where the new parents saw a Babe in swaddling clothes, angels and archangels, seraphim and cherubim saw Trinity.

That name, which started as a whisper, grew in strength as it emanated from the tiny cave. First it enveloped the blue orb. For a few seconds, all of creation froze in a moment of reverence. The fallen angels, unaware of Yahweh's plans, twisted in utter confusion as the name Jesus echoed throughout the depths of hell. As hard as they tried to hold their ears, the Name boomed and rendered the totality of the enemy's realm mute and unconscious. The Name moved through all of the created order and broke through to eternity where the Father waited, absorbing it above all names back into Himself.

The Advent had arrived and the blue orb's great silence had come to an end. But it was not just the voice of Yahweh that ended the silence. His very Being was enfleshed on the earth. He was a God who came after His lost people. The name of Jesus would bring hope and salvation from this point forward. Past, present, and future would be touched by Him.

Mary, having fed the child, put the sleeping Babe back into His crib. "I am very tired Joseph. I must rest." Joseph put his arm over Mary, becoming a blanket of warmth and comfort. As she faded off to sleep, Mary asked one last question, "Do you think anyone will remember this night?" "I don't know, my love, but that won't matter because we certainly will. Goodnight my little Jesus." The father kissed his child and fell fast asleep next to his bride.

Silent night, holy night, All is calm, all is bright,
round yon virgin mother and child.
Holy infant so tender and mild,
sleep in heavenly peace. Sleep in heavenly peace.

Silent night, holy night, Son of God, love's pure light,
radiant beams from thy holy face,
with the dawn of redeeming grace,
Jesus, Lord, at thy birth. Jesus, Lord, at thy birth.

You are the Father whom I adore,
You are the Son forevermore;
You are the Spirit that has been sent.
Blessed Trinity, help me understand Your Advent.

Adapted from "Silent Night" by Joseph Mohr (1818)

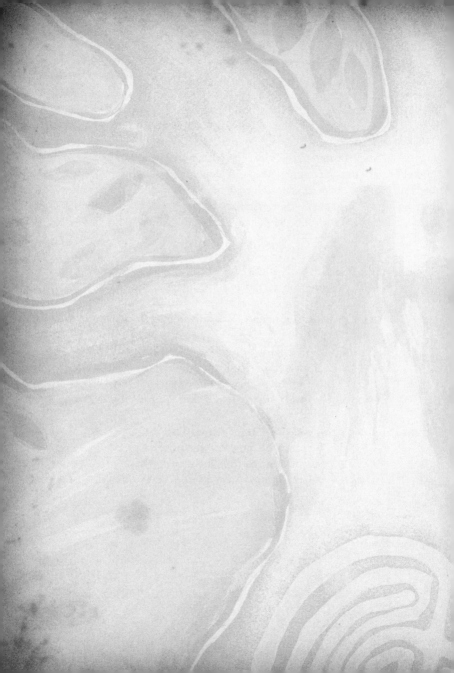

PART IV
Epiphany

and lo, the **star**, which they **saw in** the **east**, **went before them.**

Matthew 2:9b (ASV)

Star

> "Wherever we taste the truth, God is there."
> **St. Augustine,** *Confessions* **(Book IV, Chapter 12)**

> *I see him, but not right now,*
> *I perceive him, but not right here;*
> *A star rises from Jacob*
> *a scepter from Israel.*
> **Numbers 24:17a (THE MESSAGE)**

My young students, to finally discover that which you have pursed for untold years and to find yourself fleeing for your life is quite unexpected." Artaban began to chuckle as he often did when he told his story. "But I have started at the end. I must first tell you of the unlikely key that unlocked my quest. It happened on the darkest of nights. . . ." His young students sat around the fire, rapt in the mystical stories Artaban wove around the evening flame. This story was his favorite. Out of all the countless legends of heroes and creation, mystery and history, none compared with the day he bowed before the One.

His parents brought him to the city of Ecbatana as a small child. Immediately identified as a child of promise, Artaban was given to be raised in the mysterious ways of the Magi. His parents knew they would never see him again for he had been kissed by the sacred flame. By day, as a young boy, Artaban played on the fruit-filled hills of Mount Orontes. But he spent his evening being educated in the mysteries of the Magi: keepers of the Holy Flame. By the time he was a young man, Artaban had studied the holy words, prophecies, and religious rituals of several known cultures. As a Zoroaster priest he had to choose one specific religious discipline. He chose to become an expert in the ways of the Hebrews. The ultimate ambition of the Magi, recorded in the sacred writings of the Avesta, was to uncover revelations of the One True God amongst the multitude of religious expressions in the empire.

Artaban found himself drawn to the ways of a people captured by the Babylonians more than six hundred years prior. They were different than the multitude of nations that had been taken captive in the years of conquest. The Hebrews worshiped only one God. They claimed this God, Yahweh, as the All-Powerful, All-Knowing, All-Loving God and that all other gods were stick, stone, and rubble. This God was strangely akin to the Magi's Ahura Mazda, the Supreme One. He created a pilgrim people stubbornly set on serving Him alone. The darker days of Hebrew history recorded their betrayal of Yahweh. And many of their prophets proclaimed that their sins would be dealt with severely. If they rejected Yahweh they would be under the thumb of foreign invaders.

Five-hundred years ago the Persians captured the Babylonians, Medes, and Lydians under the leadership of Cyrus the Mighty. The Babylonian oppressor was now the oppressed. The Hebrew Daniel, greater than all the Magi of his day, rose to be the second most powerful man in Persia. Most believed this experience is what drew the Magi into a single religious society and how they became advisers in the courts of the Empire. Because the Hebrews and their God were carefully intertwined with the fabric of mankind's history, Artaban dedicated his life to knowing the ways of these "chosen" people by learning their holy writings and studying their prophecies.

Seeing his young pupils settled in for the evening voyage, Artaban continued his word weaving. "I sat on Mount Orontes during that black, starless night staring toward the west, toward the city of Jerusalem, pondering the prophecies of the Jewish sages. A promise, throughout their history, was scattered in their holy words. One called the 'Messiah' was to someday appear. He would bring a Holy Fire that would cleanse the earth." A young boy asked, "Is this Messiah to be a warrior sent from Ahura Mazda?" Artaban smiled at the boy's inquisitiveness. "That, Tigranes, I was unsure about. Nevertheless, I sat, as I did many evenings, wondering how this King would appear as promised in the far-away land of Israel. It was then that the star appeared. I say star because I do not know how else to explain the manifestation. Above me, like a falling missile, a light appeared. I stared in both terror and wonder for the light moved as a bolt of lightning. For just a fraction of time the heavens were filled with beings of light—gods of fire. The world was aflame. Then the leader of the star gods pointed toward the land of the Hebrews and in an instant they had crossed the distant horizon." Artaban waited as he looked at a group of boys whose eyes were the size of saucers. "Then what?" said Tigranes. "I thought you would never ask," said Artaban. He loved this part of the story.

We three kings of Orient are
Bearing gifts we traverse afar.
Field and fountain, moor and mountain,
Following yonder star.
O star of wonder, star of night,
Star with royal beauty bright,
Westward leading, still proceeding,
Guide us to thy perfect Light.

"The Quest of the Magi" (Part I), John Henry Hopkins Jr. (1857)

Then the **cloud** covered the **Tent of Meeting**, and the **glory** of the **LORD** filled the tabernacle.

Exodus 40:34 (NIV)

Glory

Those who attempt to search into the majesty of God will be overwhelmed with its glory.

Thomas á Kempis, *The Imitation of Christ*

There were sheepherders camping in the neighborhood. They had set night watches over their sheep. Suddenly, God's angel stood among them and God's glory blazed around them. They were terrified. The angel said, "Don't be afraid. I'm here to announce a great and joyful event that is meant for everybody, worldwide: a Savior has just been born in David's town, a Savior who is Messiah and Master. This is what you're to look for: a baby wrapped in a blanket and lying in a manger. At once the angel was joined by a huge angelic choir singing God's praises: Glory to God in the heavenly heights, Peace to all men and women on earth who please him.

Luke 2:8–14 (The Message)

Unlike the surrounding bustling towns, this rich valley nestled between the hills of Jerusalem and Bethlehem was blissfully quiet. Beneniah loved the hush. Standing still, he shut his eyes and listened. He could hear the soft crunching of sheep feeding on fresh grass while the bell of the lead sheep barely tinkled. Every so often Beneniah could hear some shouting or laughter that carried itself on the windless night from the City of Bread. He was thankful to be out of the ruckus. He loved his flock and considered shepherding to be a call. Whenever he ventured into town for supplies or to visit family, he would often notice a townsperson holding their nose. Someone would usually yell, "Get back to your flock! You are stinking up the whole village." Beneniah would respond, "Would you have said the same to King David? For he was a shepherd before a King and in his work I rejoice." That usually hushed any cruel words.

Beneniah clucked his tongue in the rhythmic pattern that caused his sheep to stop whatever they were doing and gather around him. His sheep knew the voice of their shepherd and would only respond to his specific call. Leading his small flock across the fields toward the large enclosure, Beneniah prepared himself as the gatekeeper for the evening. His watch would last a few hours until the moon, just entering the horizon, was high overhead. The other shepherds had already moved their flocks into the enclosure. They were gathered around a communal fire enjoying each other's company over an evening meal. Once settled, Beneniah waved over to his fellow shepherds. Lying in the front of the lone opening of the enclosure with his back against the stone and his feet propped up on the other side of the opening, Beneniah became a gate. Anything that wanted to enter or depart must go through him.

One of his fellow shepherds brought him warm bread and a bit of wine. "Can you believe how quiet it is tonight?" His friend smiled as he handed him the bread. "I thank God for these predictable, uneventful days." Beneniah stopped talking as his friend's face started to illuminate as if he was sitting in front of a growing fire. A source of marvelous light as intense as a pillar of fire was approaching rapidly across the horizon from the northeast. His friend dropped the skin of wine and stared in a stupor, causing Beneniah to turn around quickly, but as he did he fell backward over the low stones in the entrance of the sheepfold. The panicked flock rushed the gatekeeper looking for escape. Beneniah froze as the sheep, suddenly breaking for the fields, jumped and cleared his body to escape the coming explosion. Not one of the shepherds tried to stop the flocks or even seemed to take notice. They were all looking at the emerging sky-manifestation.

Though the heavenly light was too bright to gaze at, not one of the shepherds looked away. They stood in fear, assuming the end of the world had come as a phoenix hurtled toward the earth. But the phoenix did stop, hovering over the little hovel of terrified shepherds. Too brilliant to read any sort of expression, the figure soared as a god. The only sound was a symphonic hum of a million angels wanting to explode in praise. Beneniah's fraught curiosity caused him to say, "Why are you here?" The Voice spoke with excitement saying, "Do not be afraid. I am the bearer of good news. A great joy has arrived for all of humanity! At this moment, in the town of David, the Savior, the Messiah, the Lord of all has been born! Go! Find Him for He is wrapped in swaddling clothes and sleeps in a simple manger."

The shepherds would have thought the whole exchange absurd had they not been knocked to the ground by the appearance of a million times a million heavenly beings too terrible and wonderful to describe. The angels sang as one, "Glory to God, Lord of the heavenly and earthly realms who brings peace among the men and women whom please Him!" And although the glory faded, its residue remained in the hearts of the shepherds for the rest of their lives.

The Lord is my shepherd and in Him I want for nothing.
He guides me rest in my all too chaotic life,
and He leads me to still waters, where I can drink of Life.
My soul is restored as I follow His ways and not my own.

Even when I walk through terrifying and dark times,
the fear of death, the fear of anything evil falls by the wayside.
Even as my enemies surround me, He provides abundantly,
and His presence overflows through me to others.

I follow His path knowing the Father watches over me.
I follow His path knowing the Son walks by my side.
I follow His path knowing the Spirit encompasses me.
Blessed Trinity, help me understand Your Epiphany.

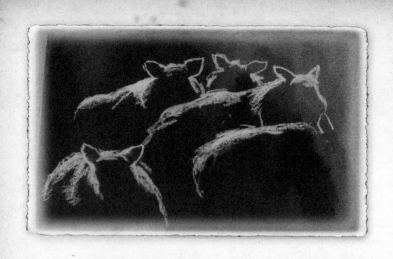

I am the Gate.
Anyone who goes through me
will be cared for—
will freely go
in and out,
and find pasture.

John 10:7 (The Message)

Shepherds

It is the unusual event, not the routine,
that carves the place in memory.
Jim Forest, *The Road to Emmaus*

When the angels went away from them into heaven, the shepherds said
one to another, Let us go over to Bethlehem and see this thing (saying)
that has come to pass, which the Lord has made known to us. So they
went with haste and [by searching] found Mary and Joseph, and the
Baby lying in a manger. And when they saw it, they made known what
had been told them concerning this Child, And all who heard it were
astounded and marveled at what the shepherds told them. But Mary
was keeping within herself all these things (sayings), weighing and
pondering them in her heart. And the shepherds returned, glorifying
and praising God for all the things they had heard and seen, just as it
had been told them.

Luke 2:15–20 (AMP)

Beneniah, along with the other shepherds, awoke from the angelic encounter a few minutes later. Unfathomable bliss had rendered all of them unconscious. After lifting himself off the ground, Beneniah helped the other shepherds to their feet. Once they had their bearings, he turned to them, speaking with decisiveness. "Why are we waiting in this field? We must go to Bethlehem and find our Shepherd!"

They climbed toward town at a steady but unhurried pace. Determined to find the Messiah, the shepherds assumed they would follow the crowds to Israel's newborn Messiah. But no one in Bethlehem acted like they knew of the angelic disturbance. In fact, it seemed as if the shepherds were the only ones who had been struck by Yahweh's glory, the good news of His Son. Merchants, peddlers, and food vendors carried on life as usual. Even the priests seemed to walk through the streets unconcerned about any sort of heavenly epiphany. Had the shepherds not had the experience together, any one of them might have thought himself mad.

The more they explored the city and the more unaware the population appeared, the more anxious the small band of shepherds grew. Beneniah thought about King David who, under Yahweh's leading, rose from shepherding the very fields where he tended his flocks now, to becoming the greatest King of Israel. That same shepherd, David, would proclaim the coming of the Messiah throughout the Psalms. Was God, once again, proclaiming His love through this ragtag group of smelly sheep-tenders?

Their treasure hunt had become much easier with the hint from the angelic being, "You shall find Him in a manger." Mangers were only found in stables and Bethlehem held only a certain amount of stables. For the first hour, the crowded streets parted like the Red Sea as the reeking group traveled to each one asking the stable-master, "We are here to worship the newborn Messiah!" The responses from any people standing around at the time varied. Most of the time, people laughed hysterically until the shepherds left embarrassed. A couple of times they were chased away by someone with a pitch-fork, and one priest called them "stinking-drunken blasphemers."

By the time they reached one of the last stables sitting on the edge of town, their spirits were depleted. The shepherds wondered if they were insane. Beneniah knew this particular stable sat behind and under the inn, so he told the others to wait for him while he checked. He would peek inside to see, if by chance, the Child was dwelling amongst a stable full of donkeys, sheep, and goats.

Beyond the stable door, Beneniah sensed a calm as if a pocket of peace had taken root in this one earthly spot. He found himself tiptoeing to the caretaker's niche. A small crackling fire illuminated a couple lying asleep on a pile of hay. In front of them lay a manger and in that manger lay a wrapped newborn. Quietly rushing to the dejected group of shepherds, Beneniah signaled for them to follow but remain silent. They worked their way back into the stable where not a single animal made a noise. Gathering around the makeshift crib they stared, unmoving. Mary and Joseph awoke to the silent group of shepherds standing in a semi-circle around the manger. Their hands were upraised and their dusty cheeks were tear-streaked.

Joseph asked why they had come, and as Beneniah told the story of God's Glory and their hunt for the Messiah, Joseph rejoiced. But Mary kept quiet. She picked up the baby and looked into his innocent eyes, pondering His future and the way the world would soon change. Beneniah and his friends were from that day forward known as the praising shepherds. And if any traveler happened to share their fire they would hear the tale of the night the Glory fell and the Messiah who still loved shepherds, no matter how bad they smelled.

There is a hunt that You have placed in my heart,
a desire to find the Savior who calls to me.
It is a pilgrimage that lasts a lifetime
and its only fulfillment shall come when I am reunited with Christ.

And in that day, after the veil of flesh has faded away
to a body gloriously resurrected and new in You,
will I begin to understand that it is You, not I,
who was the Hunter that sought my heart as your prey.

Father of life, shepherd me this morning.
Son of peace, illumine this day.
Spirit of time and eternity, enfold me this night.
Blessed Trinity, help me understand Your Epiphany.

For throughout **all** their
journeys the cloud
of the Lord was upon the
tabernacle by day, and **fire**
was in it by night.

Exodus 40:38 (AMP)

Magi

Truth is truth, whether from the lips of Jesus or Balaam.
George MacDonald, *The New Name*

After Jesus was born in Bethlehem in Judea, during the time of King Herod, Magi from the east came to Jerusalem.
Matthew 2:1 (NIV)

Artaban knew he had caused a hunger in the boys that could not be denied for long. Pulling a bit of dust from his pocket, he tossed it into the fire which suddenly took on an emerald hue and sighed like a desert owl. The boys jumped at his magic trick. "I knew I had witnessed a sign. I ran as quickly as possible to the council chambers of the Elders, the Chamber of Dreams. A thin curtain of light was already glowing from the Chamber, where my master, the Rab-Mag sat in evening contemplation. The Chamber of Dreams was alive with excited conversation. Our Master was a tall, dark man with firm lines graven around his fine thin lips; he carried the brow of a dreamer and the mouth of a soldier. He listened without a show of emotion.

"I was not the only one who witnessed the heavenly envoy that night. Several of my brothers had also gathered, disturbed by the sudden appearance of the star but they could only guess at its meaning. Gaspar, Melchior, and Balthasar, all argued that it was a sign of future destruction for the surrounding countries. Lavandad laughed and said that anyone educated in astrology knew that this was merely a crossing of the planets. Hormisdas and Gushnasaph thought it a simple blessing from Ahura Mazda; Kagba and Badadilma, probably the wisest of the small gathering, said they needed more evidence before any judgments were made about the sky-spectacle. It was then that Rab-Mag asked us, 'What do the prophecies we have studied say about such an event?'

"And I answer, 'Master, I have a thought.' I felt the hairs stand up on my arms as my fellow Magi looked in my direction. For the next few hours, I shared the story of the Hebrews. I followed their creation tale through the call of their patriarch Abraham. He was the first to embrace Yahweh as the All. I wove the tales of a captive people following a flame through the Arabian Desert and the conquering of their homeland from pagan tribes. I spoke of the Poet-Warrior David and the rise and fall of the children of Yahweh. As the sun rose in the east, I shared of their captivity by Babylon and finally how they came to live amongst our lands, for many did not return with Nehemias when the mighty Cyrus set them free.

"Throughout the long tale I shared the promises of their coming Messiah, bringer of the Holy Fire. A God-King was to be born in the land of Israel and He would be Yahweh's greatest gift and epiphany to man. I asked the gathering: 'Could it be possible that this God-King has arrived?' 'Many cultures claim a god-king, Artaban.' Lavandad was always our greatest skeptic. My reply was swift. 'We know this, but we are the keepers of the flame, the seekers of Ahura Mazda, the One True God. And none of us would be standing in this chamber had we not seen the star. Could it be possible, the God we seek has sent us a sign, a flame to follow through the desert to find that which we seek with all of our hearts? Could this be like the flame that led the Hebrews out of Egypt?'

"Children, they were as silent as you are right now. No one spoke for several agonizing minutes. We awaited the judgment of the Rab-Mag. What would he do with this knowledge? Finally the master stood. Clearing his throat he looked at all of his students sitting at his feet. His eyes smiled while his mouth held its stern position. 'It seems, my Magi, we have a quest to fulfill. We must follow the signs wherever they may take us. Artaban, it looks like you must begin to prepare for a long journey. It seems you will be taking a pilgrimage with your brother-Magi.'"

The children could not hold back their questions any longer. "Did you go?" asked young Rhodaspes. "Child, when the Magi are a given a key, the door must be opened. All those attending our midnight meeting, the Star-Gazers as they became known, would journey with me. Weeks of careful preparation had to go into an expedition that would last several months. Gifts for the God-King had to be carefully selected. My younglings, it was thrilling to think we Magi were about to follow a path set by angels! And when the day of departure arrived, not even the doubting Lavandad would have given up his place. We now joined the same wilderness paths that the released captives of Babylonia, the Hebrews of Egypt, and the Patriarch Abram took to follow the One True God to a land of promise."

> Born a king on Bethlehem's plain,
> Gold I bring to crown Him again,
> King forever, ceasing never
> Over us all to reign.
> O star of wonder, star of night,
> Star with royal beauty bright,
> Westward leading, still proceeding,
> Guide us to thy perfect Light.

"The Quest of the Magi" (Part II), John Henry Hopkins Jr. (1857)

Sanctify
(consecrate, set apart)
to Me all the
firstborn [males].

Exodus 13:2a (AMP)

Presentation

I've become sacramental because of the Incarnation . . . the Incarnation affirms that God acted through material creation to give us his salvation . . . Once I was willing to give up a spiritual spirituality and accept a spirituality rooted in creation and incarnation, in mundane things like water, oil, bread, and wine, as well as people and incidents, I was on the road to becoming sacramental.

Robert E. Webber, *Evangelicals on the Canterbury Trail*

When the eighth day arrived, the day of circumcision, the child was named Jesus, the name given by the angel before he was conceived. Then when the days stipulated by Moses for purification were complete, they took him up to Jerusalem to offer him to God as commanded in God's Law: "Every male who opens the womb shall be a holy offering to God," and also to sacrifice the "pair of doves or two young pigeons" prescribed in God's Law.

Luke 2:21–24 (THE MESSAGE)

Over the last few days the crowds drained from Bethlehem like a slowly leaking cask. With their Roman tax obligations fulfilled, most people wanted to return to their distant villages as soon as possible. But for Joseph and Mary, life was becoming a greater tangle of complexities. With the birth of a son, Mary would be unfit for travel for a few months and there was the necessity of the Child's circumcision and Mary's purification offerings. The little bit of money they possessed helped move them from stable to inn, but the manger would have to remain as a crib for a few more days.

On the eighth day after His birth, the son of Mary and Joseph was presented to a priest for circumcision. Mary cringed as she heard her child scream in pain for the first time. It would not be the last. The priest asked Joseph the son's name. "Jesus. His name is Jesus." Crinkling his wrinkled forehead, the priest replied, "Jehovah is Salvation. That is a name worthy of a leader." With a kind smile and aged hands, the priest lifted the child over his head and shouted as if the entire Promised Land was listening, "HIS NAME SHALL BE JESUS." Normally a crowd of family and friends would have erupted in celebration, but father, mother, and the priest were the only ones present. Their families did not even know of the birth. Yet the joy in hearts of the new parents could not have been contained in a thousand onlookers. "What a strange and quiet way for the Messiah to enter the world," whispered Mary in Joseph's ear, causing him to shiver with the tickle of her breath. Handing the tiny baby back to Mary, the aged priest smiled again. "I have a feeling that Yahweh has enormous plans for this one." Mary and Joseph answered his observation with deep, joyous laughter.

Joseph's first priority was to find a temporary dwelling for the growing family and then to move the baby from manger to crib. Finding a local carpenter, Joseph asked if he could exchange two days of work for the materials and tools to build a crib for his newborn son. Rubbing his black tuft of hair, the master-carpenter squinted, giving him the look of a shrewd merchant. In reality, he had become nearsighted. He was sympathetic to Joseph's plight and a bit lonely because he was a childless widower.

Over the next three days, Joseph impressed the master-carpenter with his dogged pace and unusual skill for detail. The master delighted in the particular design and careful carvings Joseph added to the crib. Joseph was both pragmatic and artistic, something rarely found in a woodworker. Walking out of the carpenter's shed on the third day, Joseph carried both a gift for his child and a job. Mary was even more surprised to find out that the master-carpenter invited the stranded family to live with him. He delighted in the possibility of filling his quiet empty home with the young family. Within a fortnight, God had provided abundantly for them as promised.

The weeks passed quickly and the newlyweds thrived in the bustling town of Bethlehem. Two months after the birth of their Miracle Child, they walked the road to Jerusalem, hand in hand. They jabbered like Greek philosophers. Bethlehem was becoming home and the thought of staying for a season was warming to them. Today marked the end of Mary's weeks of purification required by the Law. It would also be the day of their official presentation of their firstborn to God. Unable to afford a lamb, Joseph carried a pair of ivory turtle-doves as a sacrificial gift.

The ceremony was simple and uneventful. As he touched the wall of the Temple, Joseph acknowledged the history that marked this place. Looking at his baby boy, just now starting to take notice of the world around him, Joseph wondered about a world where God walked among his chosen people, like a man, yet not just a man. It was too much to decipher. Today he was just a baby; their baby. But the day was not as quiet as they imagined, as curious eyes approached as fast as a pair of elderly legs could carry them.

We are asked to trust in the Lord with all our heart.
But I keep finding more of my heart that wavers.
You implore me to not lean on my own understanding
but that is the staff I am most comfortable leaning on.

I know that in all my ways I should acknowledge You, Lord,
but sometimes that seems too simple, too unimportant.
Tame my restless, selfish heart that I may obey You
and allow You to direct and guide my life.

Father, enfold, surround, and speak to me.
Son, be in my life, on my lips, and in my heart.
Spirit, be with me in my waking, my watching, my hoping.
Blessed Trinity, help me understand Your Epiphany.

I will give you as a
covenant for
the people,
a light for
the nations.

Isaiah 42:6b (ESV)

Simeon

Several years before his death, a remarkable rabbi, Abraham Joshua Heschel, suffered a near fatal heart attack. His closest male friend was at his bedside. Heschel was so weak he was only able to whisper: "Sam, I feel only gratitude for my life, for every moment I have lived. I am ready to go. I have seen so many miracles during my lifetime." The old rabbi was exhausted by his effort to speak. After a long pause, he said, "Sam, never once in my life did I ask God for success or wisdom or power or fame. I asked for wonder, and he gave it to me."

Brennan Manning, *The Ragamuffin Gospel*

In Jerusalem at the time, there was a man, Simeon by name, a good man, a man who lived in the prayerful expectancy of help for Israel. And the Holy Spirit was on him. The Holy Spirit had shown him that he would see the Messiah of God before he died. Led by the Spirit, he entered the Temple. As the parents of the child Jesus brought him in to carry out the rituals of the Law, Simeon took him into his arms and blessed God: God, you can now release your servant; release me in peace as you promised. With my own eyes I've seen your salvation; it's now out in the open for everyone to see: A God-revealing light to the non-Jewish nations, and of glory for your people Israel.

Luke 2:25–32 (THE MESSAGE)

There was not a single person in the Eastern Quarter who could remember a day the old man had not zig-zagged through the tight stone alleys as he ambled toward his daily pilgrimage. The rhythm of his steps echoing off the thick limestone that surrounded him like eternal battlements carried his sing-song shuffle through the air. Each street produced a different cadence. Long ago, the ancient man had learned to use the tempo of his step-echoes to keep time as he sang the Psalms. His neighbors always knew he was coming and the alleyways became strangely mute at the same time every day as the holy man made his way toward the Temple of Jerusalem. Before most of the residents of the City of David were born, Simeon's songs had already become an established part of daily life. Observers from around the city often arrived in time to hear the beloved man's deep voice singing the promises of Messiah in perfect time to the beat of his footsteps. Simeon had become an established element of the City of David.

His call was rare in the days of silence. The elderly Simeon was considered by many to walk in the same spirit as the prophets of antiquity. No one denied that the Spirit of Yahweh was upon him. And no one in all of Israel, including the High Priest, visited the Temple as frequently as Simeon. As a young man, he had an epiphany that would curve the direction of his sails. Not even those closest to Simeon knew the details of what happened during his otherworldly encounter, but all heard the results of his experience in his songs. He was convinced that he would not pass from the world until he saw the Messiah in the flesh. Because of his renowned godliness, there were few that laughed at or mocked his claim, but most assumed it was more of the wish of an abundant imagination than a word from God.

This assurance projected Simeon into a lifetime of prayer for Messiah's promised return. As he visited the Temple Mount daily, he would often be heard praying words like, "Seed of Abraham we await your advent!" or "Son of David, the chosen People are desperate for Your return." Although most believed Messiah would one day appear, they did not guess that it would be within their lifetime. The promise of Messiah always seemed mythic and hazy. Yet they stood in bewilderment at Simeon's steadfast adherence: "I will see the Messiah in my lifetime."

As he grew older, and death came closer, his excitement grew. Some would say that the elderly man was increasing in giddiness almost like a small child about to receive a precious gift. Indeed, his pace never slacked. Sometimes he would leap like a gazelle all the way to the Temple. As death crept closer so did the promise. Many envied Simeon's ability to look at death as a gift rather than avoid it like an imminent shadow of doom.

On this day, upon entering into the Temple Courtyard, Simeon found his feet frozen for the first time ever. He noticed the poor couple just finishing the dedication of their young child. They were laughing and rejoicing, holding their young one above their heads as if to show him the beauty of Solomon's Temple. Simeon saw the child, not with the eyes of man, but through the lens of God. "He" was here, at this very moment. Before he could take in his next breath, Simeon was walking as fast as his legs could carry him. The parents of the Messiah-Child saw the elderly man and returned his infectious smile. "May I hold your baby and bless him?" asked Simeon. Mary stared at his kind face then handed him the tight bundle. Looking into the big brown eyes of the baby boy, Simeon began to cry. Tapping his foot on the ground to keep time, he began to sing in his familiar voice. "Yahweh, your servant is free! In Your peace, I am released; for Your promise is in my hands. My eyes have beheld Salvation—and all of the world will see! A God who arrives in the flesh not only to the chosen but all mankind; the glory of Israel revealed." A small crowd had gathered as if they were watching a street performance, but one broke from the crowd. Joseph could only wonder what this elderly woman was about to add to the performance.

> **You have promised throughout Your word,**
> **I am coming again.**
> **You have given Your promise to a desperate world,**
> **I am coming again.**
>
> **But that promise seems hazy, a myth to bring hope.**
> **And I find it hard to fathom, that You could return in my lifetime.**
> **Yet Your promise remains**
> **I am coming again.**
>
> **Only the Father knows the hour of the return.**
> **And the Son promises to return.**
> **May the Spirit prepare me for the return.**
> **Blessed Trinity, help me understand Your Epiphany.**

But standing
by the **cross**
of **Jesus** were
his mother . . .

John 19:25 (ESV)

XXXVI
Anna

"My heart is afraid that it will have to suffer," the boy confided to the Alchemist as they looked upon a moonless night. "Tell your heart that the fear of suffering is worse than the suffering itself," the Alchemist replied. "And that no heart has ever suffered when it goes in search of its dreams, because every second of the search is a second's encounter with God and eternity. We are afraid of losing what we have, whether it's our life or our possessions and property. But this fear evaporates when we understand that our life stories and the history of the world were written by the same hand."

Paulo Coelho, *The Alchemist*

And his father and his mother marveled at what was said about him. And Simeon blessed them and said to Mary his mother, "Behold, this child is appointed for the fall and rising of many in Israel, and for a sign that is opposed (and a sword will pierce through your own soul also), so that thoughts from many hearts may be revealed." And there was a prophetess, Anna, the daughter of Phanuel, of the tribe of Asher. She was advanced in years, having lived with her husband seven years from when she was a virgin, and then as a widow until she was eighty-four. She did not depart from the temple, worshiping with fasting and prayer night and day. And coming up at that very hour she began to give thanks to God and to speak of him to all who were waiting for the redemption of Jerusalem.

Luke 2:33–38 (ESV)

The woman who hobbled through the crowd upon hearing Simeon's excited blessing of the baby Jesus looked older than the Patriarchs. As she smiled, Mary could not tell where the smile on her face began and the wrinkles ended. Though her appearance was frail, as if she could break if caught in a strong breeze, Mary sensed she possessed a strength only contained in one whose life had been immersed in the love of Yahweh.

Simeon continued in his prophetic song as if he carried the future as easily as he held the small child in his arms. Walking over to Joseph and Mary, he handed the Baby back. He placed his sizeable hands on their foreheads like the branches of a massive oak reaching to the wind and blessed them in the name of the Lord of Israel. Joseph felt as though a blessing that had been waiting from the foundation of the world had finally been released. Stopping for a moment, Simeon looked at the Child's mother with the compassion of one about to share the news of an untimely death. Mary felt her muscles tighten as if preparing herself for a blow.

"You will see that this child will become the rise and fall for many throughout the Promised Land. He will be God's greatest sign. The opposition against Him will be overwhelming and His presence will unmask the true intentions of all who come in near Him." Mother and father pulled their child close to them as if they could protect Him from the overwhelming tide of His future. For the first time in months, Mary felt a shade of fear. The kindly man spoke again, "And you will feel as if a sword has pierced the depths of your soul."

Mary almost collapsed under the weight of Simeon's words, but her stand was steadied as the gnarled hands of the ancient matriarch cupped Mary's face. She held her cheeks in her hands the way only a grandmother would know how to do. The old woman, Anna, was known to all who visited the Temple regularly. If Simeon was the last of the prophets, Anna was the last of the prophetesses.

The story had been passed down that Anna had become a bride at a very young age but only seven years into the marriage, her husband experienced an untimely death. With no desire to remarry, Anna dedicated herself, like her contemporary Simeon, to Yahweh. The Temple would become her home. She was well known for her unwavering prayers. When one was desperate they always found their way to the aged woman. Many times she found her way to thcm in thcir moments of distress. Fasting was her only steady diet. Now, at eighty-four, Anna carried a place in the hearts of many and was revered as much as the High Priest.

Holding Mary's face, she pulled her close whispering potent prayers, infusing the young mother with the same deep trust she had experienced when the angel Gabriel spoke to her of the miracle baby. Turning to the crowd that had become uncomfortably quiet, Anna prayed aloud to Yahweh while looking deep into the eyes of the surrounding audience. She spoke of her God's promises and her thanksgiving for His faithfulness. She reminded the growing Temple crowd of the coming of the Seed of Abraham, the One who was in their midst. "God is near and the redemption of Israel draws nigh! His Light has shined for those who have eyes to see! His mouth speaks for all who are willing to hear!"

Later in the afternoon, as the young couple walked back to their temporary home in Bethlehem they wondered aloud at what the future held for their child. Mary spoke to her husband, "We cannot begin to guess what lies ahead. What is assured is that we seem to be following in the footsteps of our babe, who has not yet walked upon the earth."

And a few hundred miles to the east, another group of strangers were treading that same path.

Sometimes I want to know the future,
what lies ahead in the path You offer me.
But I am fairly certain that if You were to show me,
I would turn away in selfishness or fear.

Please, Lord, show me only what I need to know.
Help me to trust in the paths You lead me on.
Remind me that You never take me anywhere
that You will not walk by my side.

To the Father who carries me over jagged rocks and torrid streams.
And the Son who straightens crooked passes.
And the Spirit who lifts me out of destructive pits.
Blessed Trinity, help me understand Your Epiphany.

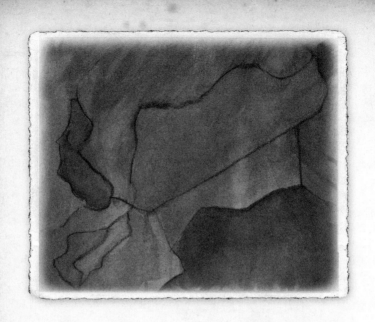

I will also make you a
light for
the Gentiles,
that you may bring my
salvation to the ends
of the
earth.

Isaiah 49:6b (NIV)

XXXVII

Arrival

The Road goes ever on and on
Down from the door where it began.
Now far ahead the Road has gone,
And I must follow, if I can,
Pursuing it with eager feet,
Until it joins some larger way
Where many paths and errands meet.
And whither then? I cannot say.
J. R. R. Tolkien, ***The Lord of the Rings***

After Jesus was born in Bethlehem village, Judah territory—this was during Herod's kingship—a band of scholars arrived in Jerusalem from the East. They asked around, "Where can we find and pay homage to the newborn King of the Jews? We observed a star in the eastern sky that signaled his birth. We're on pilgrimage to worship him."
Matthew 2:1–2 (THE MESSAGE)

I had imagined our entry into the land of the Hebrews would have brought us great joy." Artaban continued with his story even though he was noticing the frequency of young yawns increasing. "Instead our quest seemed more in vain the closer we drew to the city of Jerusalem." Artaban took a moment to stretch, and then he offered his young pupils small cups of steaming tea to warm their bodies and arouse their minds from the sleep that was sniffing at the shadows.

"After weeks of preparation our little band of Magi was on our way. Those months of travel were some of the best days of my life. During the day, we would often stop beside wayside springs, and at night we would sleep under the guardian stars. Every so often, one of the Magi on the night watch would see a faint light in the direction of our quest. The star-light would only last a sparrow's breath, but it was enough to encourage us forward. We would pass the days discussing prophecy or pondering the mysteries of creation. Every so often the inseparable Gaspar and Melchior would throw out a crafty riddle that might keep us silent for hours as we wrested in our minds with the cunning enigma. The answer was always too simple and it would often infuriate Lavandad causing the rest of our cheerful company several more hours of mirth.

"Our journey started at the level plains of the Nisaens where we passed the famous Parthian horse herds. We traversed the fertile fields of Concabar, raising the dust from the threshing-floors like a golden mist. We passed the temple of Astarte with its four-hundred pillars and renewed our supplies at the rich gardens of Baghistan, always shadowed by the fierce brow of the Mountain of the King. If you look closely at the mount you can see the figure of King Darius trampling upon his fallen foes. By the time we left our blessed country we were becoming road-hardened.

"We moved through many a cold and desolate pass, often crawling painfully across wind-swept mesas or passing through the claws of wicked gorges; always moving southwest. Through the oak groves of Carine and the sinister Gates of Zargos we traveled. We were always thinking about the God-King. The ancient city of Chala was a welcome rest. But the sudden ease caused some in our little band to question if the quest was too difficult. Was it time to turn around for the safety of home? But that night the doubt-filled Lavandad ran to us in a sweat during his night watch. 'I saw it—the star! I looked to the southwest, like always. It started as an azure spark on the horizon born out of the darkness. Like a growing flame it started to turn purple, then erupted into a crimson sphere. Spiraling upward through rays of saffron and orange it finally exploded in white radiance. It was the star! There will be no more talk of returning. We must continue the journey.' From that day forward, Lavandad was a different man.

"The next few weeks went quickly as we passed through Ctesiphon and Selucia. Crossing the swirling Tigris we visited the shattered walls of Babylon, then we spent long weeks navigating the arid Syrian deserts. By the time we reached the borderlands of the Hebrews, we Magi had traveled more than a thousand miles. It was just over a year after the first night of the star sighting so we assumed the presence of the King was well known amongst His Hebrew subjects. But their answers to our inquiries, though greatly varied, pointed to the same fact: not one of the God-King's subjects believed He had arrived. Some would laugh at us while other villages opened doors of hospitality to our strange caravan of gentile mages. Some would even say there was always a messiah or two popping up. By the time we reached Jerusalem, the entire city was astir. The news of our arrival had preceded us. Certainly the citizens of Jerusalem knew of the star-sign and the God-King, but her citizens were agitated at our questions. Many would turn away as they saw us approaching and if we tried to talk to city leaders they always told us to keep our voices down because Herod might hear our inquiry.

"We finally held council in the upper room of a small, comfortable inn and it was decided that King Herod was the one we must see to open the next door of our mysterious quest."

Frankincense to offer have I.
Incense owns a Deity nigh.
Prayer and praising all men raising,
Worship Him, God on high.
O star of wonder, star of night,
Star with royal beauty bright,
Westward leading, still proceeding,
Guide us to thy perfect Light.

"The Quest of the Magi" (Part III), John Henry Hopkins Jr. (1857)

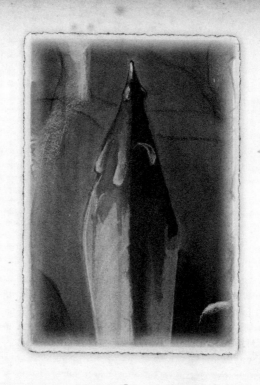

A voice is heard in
Ramah, lamentation
and bitter weeping.
Rachel is weeping for
her **children.**

Jeremiah 31:15 (ESV)

Goodness itself is a terror to anyone who clings to any evil intent.
Rolland Hein, *Christian Mythmakers*

When word of their inquiry got to Herod, he was terrified—and not Herod alone, but most of Jerusalem as well. Herod lost no time. He gathered all the high priests and religion scholars in the city together and asked, "Where is the Messiah supposed to be born?" They told him, "Bethlehem, Judah territory. The prophet Micah wrote it plainly: It's you, Bethlehem, in Judah's land, no longer bringing up the rear. From you will come the leader who will shepherd-rule my people, my Israel." Herod then arranged a secret meeting with the scholars from the East. Pretending to be as devout as they were, he got them to tell him exactly when the birth-announcement star appeared. Then he told them the prophecy about Bethlehem, and said, "Go find this child. Leave no stone unturned. As soon as you find him, send word and I'll join you at once in your worship."

Matthew 2:3–8 (THE MESSAGE)

W e had no sooner decided on a meeting with Herod than a knock came to the door. A hooded figure stood in the shadows outside of the upper room. I answered the door. The man pulled me close and whispered into my ear, 'Herod the Great wishes a private audience with your Magi. His majesty wishes to have you visit in secret for there are enemies that even now are plotting your harm. I shall return before the rooster crows. Be ready and packed. Have your servants wait outside of the city. I will lead you and the others in secret to Herod the Great.' The man vanished as quickly as he arrived, not giving us much time to prepare, but we were so close and we had journeyed so far that we did not want to miss this opportunity."

"How did Herod find out about you?" asked one of the yawning children. "King Herod was a sly fox. Rome loved him for his skills of diplomacy. But he was a ruthless man who knew how to quiet his enemies. Herod's shrewdness and quick decisions saved the Temple in Jerusalem from being sacked and defiled when Rome took residence. But when he knew that Rome placed him in power, he had all heirs to the throne slaughtered, including his own sons. It is said in that land that it is better to be Herod's hog than to be his son. But because he was Rome's lapdog, Herod was hated by the Jews. He was not a descendant of King David. Worse yet, he was an Edomite, in the lineage of Esau, so he had no right to call himself King of the Jews. Because of these facts there were always plots brewing to assassinate Herod. Herod's harsh reign had done more to promote the Hebrew's praying for Messiah than anyone else in the history of Israel. More than anything, Herod was obsessed with keeping power.

"Our arrival filled Herod with dread. When the Magi arrived at the gates of Jerusalem looking for a newborn Messiah, Herod's superstitions took possession of his mind. He could deal with false messiahs or Jewish instigators with ease, but if the population believed in the return of a true Jewish Messiah it would be a disaster beyond remedy. And the city of Jerusalem also knew that if Herod began to take our claims seriously there would be blood spilt in the streets. So Herod decided to exterminate this newborn king before he was dethroned by a zealous population awaiting deliverance. And we would be the way he located the young Messiah.

"Even as he sent his secret messenger to us, Herod gathered the finest Hebrew scholars in the city. For hours, he asked them about the 'messiah' and his advent. It was said that Herod's scream shattered the nerves of every priest gathered in his throne room. 'Where is this King to be born!' One ambitious priest looking for a handout from the volatile ruler spoke, 'It is said, my king, that the Messiah, when He arrives, will be born in Bethlehem.' Attempting to ease Herod's mood, the priest tried to convince him that if the Messiah returned they would be the first to know. Yet, Herod knew something was wrong. In fact, he became more disturbed, but a plan formed in his devious heart.

"By the time we arrived, Herod the Killer had transformed into Herod the Pious. Taking us to his private inner chamber, he served us out of his finest foods, sweet-meats, and wines. He was absorbed by our tale of the Star of the East and our long and dangerous journey that we took for the slight possibility of seeing the God-King. After exhausting every question possible, Herod shared with us the prophecy of Bethlehem. We were delighted, but still confused about how such a devout king did not know anything about the advent of his Messiah. 'Please make haste and find the Messiah-child. If he is in Bethlehem, you will find him. And when you do, send word to me for I wish to worship the true King of Israel.'

"Though we should have left excited, every one of us felt a sense of dread. Herod was up to something. Yet we were one step closer to the end of our quest."

> Myrrh is mine: Its bitter perfume
> Breaths a life of gathering gloom.
> Sorrowing, sighing, bleeding dying,
> Sealed in the stone-cold tomb.
> O star of wonder, star of night,
> Star with royal beauty bright,
> Westward leading, still proceeding,
> Guide us to thy perfect Light.

"The Quest of the Magi" (Part IV), John Henry Hopkins Jr. (1857)

To him who
knocks,
the door will
be opened.

Luke 11:10b (NIV)

The Door

Man goes far away or near but God never goes far-off; he is always standing close at hand, and even if he cannot stay within he goes no further than the door.

Meister Eckhart

Instructed by the king, they set off. Then the star appeared again, the same star they had seen in the eastern skies. It led them on until it hovered over the place of the child. They could hardly contain themselves: They were in the right place! They had arrived at the right time! They entered the house and saw the child in the arms of Mary, his mother. Overcome, they kneeled and worshiped him.

Matthew 2:9–11a (THE MESSAGE)

Some of the boys were fast asleep as Artaban continued his story. "We traveled a few miles south to the quiet city of Bethlehem. Overshadowed by the sprawling city of Jerusalem, Bethlehem did not seem the likely nursery for heavenly royalty. We changed into the clothes of common merchants so as not to draw more unwanted attention. As we came to the city gate, we privately discussed where to begin to search. Balthsas suggested, 'If we have been led all this way by the star-sign, why not ask the One who sent the sign where we are to go?'

"So we gathered around while Balthsas quietly sang the song of old, the prophecy of Balaam, as a prayer: 'We see the Ancient-New, but not now. We watch for the God-King, but know not where He lay; a Star has risen amongst the children of Jacob and the King's scepter rises from the land of Israel. O, great king, Yahweh of the Hebrews, King of Kings, Alpha and Omega, who can find You unless You reveal Yourself? We who seek You acknowledge that it is You who seeks us.' Balthsas rested but the quiet lasted only seconds before the eastern sky exploded in the brilliant light of a million suns. The star-figure hung over the village, dwarfing it with its presence. The figure was pointing into the middle of the town. Every one of the Magi saw the atmosphere afire but the other citizens of the town took no notice. They could not see the glory that we were seeing.

"Following the leading of the star-being, we came to the humble house of a poor carpenter. As the star faded, we could hardly contain ourselves. Months of travel, hundreds of miles underfoot, and thousands of years of prophecy had led us to the very doorstep of the God-King. We had not arrived at an earthly palace adorned with the abundant riches or a celestial hall filled with philosophers and magicians. Our final destination was neither the great pavilion of a terrifying warlord nor the top of the highest mountain in the world. We stood at the wooden door of a simple home in an ordinary village. Yet, this was the exact place at the exact moment in time that the star-being led us. 'What now?' asked Gushnasaph. My reply was the only thing I could think of at the time. 'It is time to knock on this door and meet the King.'

"As I knocked I could not imagine what was on the other side of the door. A young woman, quiet and beautiful, answered. At the same moment, her husband, the local carpenter, came around from the yard assuming the crowd at his door meant a big job. 'I know this will be hard to understand but I have a story to tell you.' The woman smiled and said, 'You may be surprised how many odd tales come our way.' Inviting us into their small home, they sat us down for tea and the woman started to prepare the most delicious honey cakes. Her husband, Joseph, began to wash our dusty feet while we told of our extraordinary trek. Though the couple seemed quite entertained by our tale, they did not seem the least bit surprised. They shared a look of concern when they heard of Herod's interest.

"None of us noticed the small movements on the palette that Mary sat upon. A small hand emerged from the sheepskin cover, then a leg. A plump Hebrew child crawled out from under the skin into his mother's arms. Upon seeing the child, a presence filled the atmosphere of the room. This was an overwhelming experience for us, the Magi, as if the Creator had suddenly appeared in the tiny home. We fell to our faces, prostate before the God-King in the form of a small helpless child. Children, I cannot explain to you what happened to us at that moment. Trying to put it into words seems profane. It was the One, the Messiah, like Ahura Mazda in the flesh yet much, much more. Everything we had spent our lives pursuing was contained in this Child. We wept and laughed all in the same moment. The God-Child crawled over to this silly group of blubbering sophisticated Magi now rendered helpless in the presence of the Child. The Baby started to crawl on top of Lavandad, wrapping his chubby fingers around his long nose. What else could we do but laugh?

"The rest of the evening was spent eating the most delicious bread, drinking deep of the wine Joseph provided, and talking of the future of the newborn King. It was nearly midnight before we departed but there was still the matter of our gifts that needed to be presented to the One who would forever be the focus of our worship, the key to our quest."

> Glorious now behold Him arise,
> King and God and Sacrifice.
> Alleluia, alleluia!
> Sounds through the earth and skies.
> O star of wonder, star of night,
> Star with royal beauty bright,
> Westward leading, still proceeding,
> Guide us to thy perfect Light.

"The Quest of the Magi" (Part V), John Henry Hopkins Jr. (1857)

The place where your
treasure is,
is the place you will most
want to be,
and end up
being.

Matthew 6:21 (The Message)

Treasured Escape

XL

God, as Truth, has been for me a treasure beyond price. May He be so to every one of us.

Mohandas Gandhi

Then they opened their treasures and presented him with gifts of gold and of incense and of myrrh. And having been warned in a dream not to go back to Herod, they returned to their country by another route.

Matthew 2:11b–12 (NIV)

I remember it was late in the evening. The baby Jesus was nodding off in his mother's warm embrace. Kagba and Hormisdas had returned from securing our servants and animals at a local inn. Before we departed, we reached deep into our rucksacks pulling out the costly gifts we had carried from the heart of Persia. For some reason, presenting these offerings set us into a strange formality. Seeing such a lofty group of scholars present carefully wrapped bundles to a babe would have seemed absurd if the watcher did not realize the young one was the most important of all Kings ever born.

"Along with a few other items, we presented gold, the most precious of metals signifying the purity of wisdom. We thanked God for the foresight of this gift because the family was in great need of sustenance. Hardened myrrh was presented to the God-Child. A primary ingredient of anointing oil, purification rites, and embalming, the myrrh was a reminder of the Spirit of Truth which the Magi sought and the gift of life. Our final offering was frankincense. Gaspar, during his travels in Arabia, had harvested the resin himself from several Boswellia trees. It had taken him weeks to collect a small vial's worth. The sweet odor of the resin reminded us of the fragrant sacrifices our lives are to the True God. These few sacrifices were mere sparks compared to the blazing epiphany of the Holy One that had consumed our hearts.

"We departed in tears knowing we would most likely never see the King again in this life. Within minutes of entering the inn, we lay down exhausted and in much need of rest. In minutes, the room looked like it was littered with corpses. So you can imagine our shock when we awoke to the screams of Lavandad. 'I have had the most disturbing dream. Herod was rampaging through this town and his hands were covered with the blood of infants; their screams were silenced in the blood.' Badadilma was in a sweat and shaking as he told us that a star-being appeared to him in a dream warning us not to return to Herod, as we already sensed, but to leave immediately, in the darkness of the morn.

"So that is what we did. As the others prepared the secret caravan, Lavandad and I revisited the home of the God-Child, Jesus, to tell his parents of the dream-warnings, but by the time we arrived, Joseph was loading up his donkey with a few necessary items also preparing for a night escape. 'I have also been warned in a dream. We are departing for Egypt tonight. We rest in the will of Yahweh.' Together we stood, holy family and foreign Magi, asking for safety and the wisdom of God as we went our opposite directions; the Magi crossed the deserts of Syria while Joseph, Mary, and Jesus crossed the deserts of Arabia.

"It appears all seekers eventually become desert-wanderers while obeying the voice of God. It is quite unexpected to finally discover that which you have pursued for untold years only to find yourself fleeing for your life. Quite unexpected, indeed."

Artaban looked around a room so silent you could hear the dust settle. The children were fast asleep, a few were snoring while lying atop one another. After putting wood on the fire and covering them with blankets, Artaban went into his small room. The children would certainly have stories for their parents in the morning. And, in turn, the parents would want to hear of the Quest of the Magi. But there were so many more tales to tell. Being a shepherd for Christ-followers in the land of the Persians meant always having plenty of time for more stories around the fire.

You have called me out of darkness
to seek Your Presence and Your will.
Across the arid deserts of my hardened heart,
my will, my sins, and my stubbornness.

I bring you gifts and lay them at your feet:
my mind, may it be set on You,
my soul, may it be filled by You,
my spirit, may it be alive with You!

In the name of the Father precious,
and of the Spirit of healing balm,
in the name of the Lord Jesus,
I embrace Your Epiphany.

And the
Word became flesh and
dwelt among us, and
we have
seen his glory,
glory as of the only
Son from the Father,
full of grace and truth.

John 1:14 (ESV)

Epiphany

In many ways, we see our quest for God as a trail up a mountain. God abides at the peak and we must find the path to His Presence. There are numerous trails up the mount. Do they all lead to Him? There is no easy way to know from our limited perspective what is up the mountain. Some paths may be higher or lower than others. How do we know? Look for the trail that starts from the top and leads to the bottom. Look for a religion whose God makes a path to us—not us to Him. It is insanity to think that we as Finite Beings can ever please or reach an Infinite God. We must find where He has come to us.

Peter Kreeft, *Socrates Meets Jesus*

In the beginning was the Word, and the Word was with God, and the Word was God. He was in the beginning with God. All things were made through him, and without him was not any thing made that was made. In him was life, and the life was the light of men. The light shines in the darkness, and the darkness has not overcome it.

John 1:1–5 (ESV)

A s the ancient man sunk into a peaceful sleep, Lucis continued to sit at the fire for several minutes contemplating Artaban's tale. Veiled in angelic glory, the heavenly storyteller had enjoyed the retelling of the Magi's quest that he witnessed those many earth-years ago. The heavenly chronicler slowly rolled up his parchment filled with tales of the Advent and Epiphany.

In the next moment, he was hovering over the city of Bethlehem, where countless numbers of the angelic race had rushed to at the moment of Advent to praise the newborn Son. He replayed watching the Magi caravan disappearing into the rising eastern sun the morning of their escape home while mother, father, and child headed south, their travels just beginning. Lucis took in a deep breath of the Spirit and silently praised the Creator for the call he had been given. It was time for new assignments, fresh stories, new characters, and untold adventures.

Raising his hands in surrender, Lucis spun around like a whirlwind in exaltation. Crying out with a voice he hoped echoed to the throne room of God he yelled: Glory to God in the highest, may You bring peace to Your children forever and to the ages of ages.

Gloria in Excelsis Deo

Glory to God in the highest and on earth peace,
goodwill to all people.
We praise You, we bless You, we worship You, we glorify You,
we give thanks to You for Your great glory.
Lord, King, heavenly God, Father, Almighty;
Lord, the only begotten Son, Jesus Christ, and Holy Spirit.
Lord God, Lamb of God, Son of the Father
who takes away the sin of the world,
have mercy on us, You who take away the sins of the world.
Receive our prayer, You who sit at the right hand of the Father,
and have mercy on us.
For You alone are holy, only You are Lord
Jesus Christ, to the glory of God the Father. Amen.
Each day we bless You,
and we praise Your name forever
and to the ages of ages.

A Brief History of Advent and Epiphany

Though historians are not sure when the celebration of Advent was first observed throughout Christendom, most agree that churches started establishing the seeds of the Advent season as early as the fourth century. The very nature of Advent has allowed a wide variety of local geographic traditions to spring up throughout history.

The word "Advent" comes from the Latin *adventus* which means "coming." The traditional Advent season starts between November 27 and December 3 to the Nativity of Jesus, better known as Christmas Day, December 25. Advent focuses the church on building expectancy for the celebration of the Incarnation of God, the first coming of Christ. This, in turn, prepares the followers of Christ for His eventual second coming.

For those who may wonder, the origin of the Nativity scene belongs to St. Francis of Assisi. On Christmas Eve of 1223, Francis turned a stable outside of the town of Greccio into a lesson on the Incarnation. Even though the evening was surprisingly frigid, curious townsfolk paraded down to see what the unpredictable preacher had up his sleeve. In the manger lay a tiny infant wrapped in swaddling rags. The baby was kept quite warm by the surrounding livestock. As described by John Michael Talbot in his insightful book, *The Lessons of St. Francis,* "There in that humble barn in a backwoods Italian town, the joy of Christmas became palpable through the (first) Nativity scene, a life-like reenactment of the birth of Jesus that tells volumes more about the true meaning of Christmas . . . (Francis) wanted to dive into the event, and experience it with all his senses."

Epiphany, which means "to be revealed" or "manifestation," finds its roots in the Eastern Church. Traditionally following the twelve days after Christmas ending on January 6, Epiphany celebrates the illumination of God in human form, making Epiphany the culmination of Christmas. The celebration days leading up to Epiphany commemorate Christ's manifestations of Godhood to the church, such as the wedding at Cana, His baptism, and primarily the visitation of the Magi. Epiphany is the Eastern Church's equivalent to the Western Church's Christmas season: thus the actual twelve days of Christmas. Epiphany reminds us that though the world is often swollen with darkness, the Epiphany of Christ brings God's Light to every corner. As we embrace the Epiphany of Christ, we then become a beacon to those bound and blind in the darkness.

Acknowledgments

There are always a multitude of people who are necessary in the creative process of writing:

My children, who resonate with Christmas spirit and remind me why it is worth putting the Christmas lights out every year.

My editor, Jamie Richardson, who patiently continues to teach me how to properly use the English language.

My narrative editor, Mike Flickinger, who understands narrative and the way I tell stories.

My reading team: Bonnie West, Holly O'Brien, Lori Janke, Paul McClendon, and Darryl Golwitzer for the patience to wriggle through my average writing and push me to above average.

My storytelling mentors Peggy and Gene Helmick-Richardson. Your passion for the spoken word continues to spark the sacred flame.

My church, Irving Bible, for being the first community of believers that I have ever been able to call "home." Pastor Andy, thank you for being human and knowing that fact.

The board of Wonder Voyage: Michael Fleming, Ken Janke, Tom Nichols, Sammy Chesser, and Joe Morrone. I am humbled by how much you believe in me.

The Wonder Voyage staff and voyage directors: By far, the greatest team in the world. How many thousands have you infected with your passion for Christ, your heart for adventure, and your commitment to serve the least of these?

A very special thank you to Calvin Miller, whose writings have inspired me from my first steps on the Via of Christ. Many of the prayers in this book are inspired by your book *The Path of Celtic Prayer*. Your encouraging emails to me are treasured.

Henry van Dyke's excellent short work, *The Story of the Other Wise Man,* (which I found in a Philadelphia suburb library book sale) was my primary inspiration for the retelling of the quest of the Magi. Thanks to Susan and Michael Damiano who took me to that sale unaware of the treasure I would discover.

About the Author

In 1999, after ten years as a youth minister, Shawn took a year-long sabbatical to find out what he wanted to do when he grew up. The result of that time was the launching of Wonder Voyage in the year 2000.

Wonder Voyage is a unique organization dedicated to educating and leading groups into the ancient art of pilgrimage and in life-transforming service trips around the world. Shawn has had the privilege of leading thousands of people to locations around the world that include such diverse locations as India, Fiji, Italy, Madagascar, and Peru.

Although he leads several trips and retreats a year, Shawn considers himself first and foremost a storyteller. The award-winning, *The Via Crucis,* was his first endeavor at publishing in his unique storytelling style. Several more books are on the way. He and his wife, Cheryl, reside in Texas. They have four children.

About the Artist

Jenny Slaver has been drawing since she could hold a crayon. She met Shawn Small at a camping retreat he hosted while she was still in high school. One night, around the campfire, Shawn affirmed her gift for creativity and art. Jenny claims that night as one of the first moments that she truly began to acknowledge herself as an artist. Since then, Shawn has been a diehard advocate for Jenny's art.

Wonder Voyage Missions

Wonder Voyage Missions is an extraordinary non-profit organization dedicated to providing unique, customized pilgrimages, mission trips around the world, and heart-provoking retreats. Through Wonder Voyage each event becomes a journey and every participant a pilgrim.

Wonder Voyage focuses on six primary principles:

- **Community Venture**

  Wonder Voyage desires to take communities that follow Christ and draw them nearer to the heart of God and to the hearts of each other. We are an ecumenical organization committed to the Word of God, the unity of the saints, and a living, passionate Savior.

- **Voyage of Exploration**

  At Wonder Voyage, we avoid the tourist traps and seize life. From exotic locations to remarkable experiences, Wonder Voyage takes you to the hidden scenes of life. On a Wonder Voyage, exploration and adventure are inevitable. The via crucis is just one path that we offer pilgrims along the way.

- **Customizing the Event**

  At Wonder Voyage, we recognize that every group has a unique personality. We assess your group's desires and objectives to fashion an event that will become an exceptional and personal experience for your group.

- **Encounter Moments**

  Every event consists of defining reflections that we refer to as Encounter Moments. God often orchestrates encounters for your team through exploration, storytelling, journaling, or team reflection.

- **Handling the Details**

  Wonder Voyage allows you to enjoy your event instead of juggling the vital details such as transportation, food, lodging, and coordination that often keep a team leader buried in minutia. Our experienced staff does the work and you enjoy the benefits.

- **Global Possibilities**

  Wonder Voyage is established in several locations around the world, but we are willing to go anywhere a team desires. What about a domestic pilgrimage to historic New Orleans or the sprawling streets of New York City? Or maybe you have a heart for the rolling hills of Ireland or the jungles of Costa Rica? Wonder Voyage has global possibilities.

For more information visit www.wondervoyage.com

ShawnSmallStories.com

To learn more about Shawn's other books such as the award winning, *The Via Crucis*, or to keep up with his blog, visit www.ShawnSmallStories.com.

The Via Crucis, THE FIRST BOOK IN THE VIA DEVOTIONAL SERIES, COMBINES SACRED SCRIPTURE, STORYTELLING, AND PERSONAL REFLECTION TO DRAW READERS INTO A HEARTFELT AND INSPIRING CONTEMPLATION OF JESUS' SACRIFICE AND HIS TRIUMPHANT VICTORY OVER DEATH

FOR MORE INFORMATION OR TO PURCHASE COPIES OF **The Via Crucis,** PLEASE VISIT WWW.SHAWNSMALLSTORIES.COM.